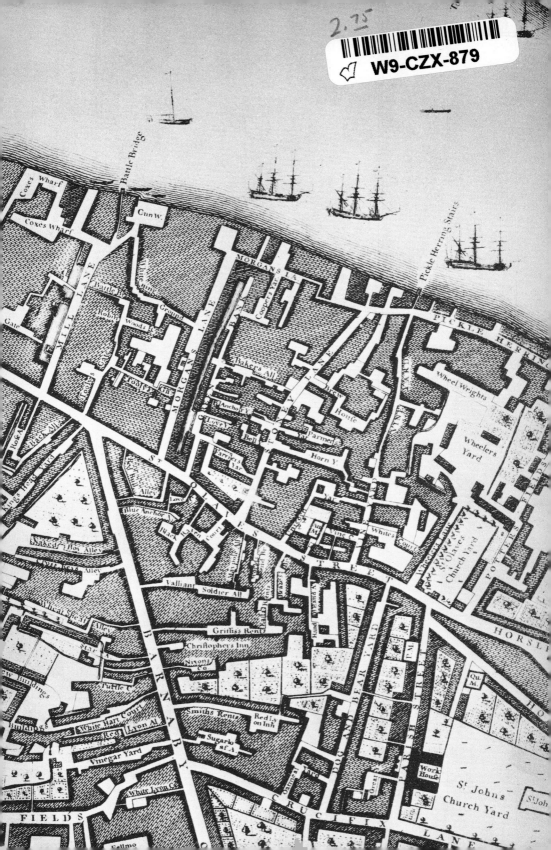

WILLIAM SHIPPEN, JR.

MEMOIRS OF THE

AMERICAN PHILOSOPHICAL SOCIETY

held at Philadelphia
for Promoting Useful Knowledge

VOLUME 28

William Shippen, Jr.   Lambdin after Stuart—Etched by H. Wright Smith.

WILLIAM SHIPPEN, JR.

PIONEER IN
AMERICAN MEDICAL EDUCATION

A BIOGRAPHICAL ESSAY

by BETSY COPPING CORNER

———————

*With NOTES, and the Original Text of Shippen's
STUDENT DIARY, London, 1759-1760; together with
a translation of his Edinburgh DISSERTATION, 1761*

———————

AMERICAN PHILOSOPHICAL SOCIETY
INDEPENDENCE SQUARE
PHILADELPHIA
1951

PRINTED IN THE UNITED STATES OF AMERICA
BY J. H. FURST COMPANY, BALTIMORE, MARYLAND

To G. W. C., the anatomist
and
G. W. C., Jr., the obstetrician

PREFACE

The preparation of this work was made possible through the generosity of Dr. J. Hall Pleasants of Baltimore who loaned William Shippen's Diary for study. Through the courtesy of the American Philosophical Society, Shippen's doctoral dissertation, a copy of which, presented to Benjamin Franklin, is in the Society's library, was also made available for study. Various letters found by search through the Shippen Papers in the collections of the Historical Society of Pennsylvania are reproduced here by permission of the Society. Dr. George W. Corner has served as anatomical consultant and has translated Shippen's dissertation, *De Placentae cum Utero Nexu*, appearing as Appendix I in the book. Dr. George W. Corner, Jr., of the obstetrical staff of Johns Hopkins Hospital, Baltimore, has interpreted in the light of modern theory the entries in Elizabeth Drinker's account of William Shippen as a practitioner of obstetrics. Dr. Cecil K. Drinker has kindly allowed the use of material from his volume, *Not So Long Ago*, based upon the diary of his ancestress. Several English correspondents have been helpful in supplying inaccessible details from British records, and full acknowledgment of their kindness appears where the information is used in the text. To all these individuals mentioned, to the libraries consulted in Baltimore, Philadelphia, Washington, and New York, to friends who encouraged the undertaking through their interest, and particularly to Dr. Pleasants, I inscribe my grateful thanks.

Using the diary as a background, I have tried to picture the small figure of a young American medical student plunged into the multifarious activities of eighteenth-century London and to show how his subsequent career was influenced by these experiences.

B. C. C.

Baltimore
October 24, 1949

vii

CONTENTS

ILLUSTRATIONS

ABBREVIATED TITLES OF SOURCES
FREQUENTLY CITED

The Ambulator: The Ambulator, or The Stranger's Tour Round London within the Circuit of Twenty-five Miles, London, 1782. Entries from this book have been transcribed whenever Shippen's diary calls for identification of a locality.

BB: *Biographia Brittanica*, ed. Robert Watt, Edinburgh, 1832.

BD: *Biographia Dramatica*, ed. David Erskine Baker, London, 1812.

Boswell's *Johnson*: James Boswell, *Life of Samuel Johnson*, ed. Roger Ingpen, 2 v., London, Pitman, 1907.

DAB: *Dictionary of American Biography*, N. Y., 1928-1937.

DNB: *Dictionary of National Biography*, London, 1808-1909.

Austin Dobson: Austin Dobson, *Eighteenth Century Vignettes*, 3 v., N. Y., Oxford Univ. Press, 1923.

Encyclopedia of London: Encyclopedia of London, ed. William Kent, N. Y., 1937.

Fielding's *Covent Garden Journal*, ed. Jensen: *Henry Fielding's Covent Garden Journal*, ed. Gerard Edward Jensen, New Haven, Yale Univ. Press, 1915.

Genest: Rev. John Genest, *Some Account of the English Stage*, Bath, 1832.

Goodman: Nathan G. Goodman, *Benjamin Rush, Physician and Citizen*, Phila., Univ. of Penna. Press, 1934.

GWC: Dr. George W. Corner.

HSP: Historical Society of Pennsylvania.

Lecky: W. E. H. Lecky, *History of England in the XVIII Century*, 7 v., N. Y., Longmans, 1918-1925.

Life of the Countess of Huntingdon: The Life and Times of Selina Countess of Huntingdon, by a member of the Houses of Shirley and Hastings, London, 1844.

Life of Esther De Berdt: William B. Reed, *The Life of Esther De Berdt afterwards Esther Reed*, Phila., 1853.

MacVickar: Rev. John MacVickar, *A Domestic Narrative of the Life of Samuel Bard, M. D., L. L. D.*, N. Y., 1822.

Montgomery: Thomas H. Montgomery, *A History of the University of Pennsylvania from Its Foundation to A. D. 1770*, Phila., Jacobs, 1900.

Morton: Thomas G. Morton, *The History of the Pennsylvania Hospital, 1751-1895*, Phila., 1895.

Munk's *Roll*: William Munk, *The Roll of the Royal College of Physicians*, 2nd ed., London, 1878.

OED: *Oxford English Dictionary*, 10 v., and supp., Oxford, 1888-1933.

Packard: Francis R. Packard, *History of Medicine in the United States*, 2 v., N. Y., Hoeber, 1932.

Parsons: F. G. Parsons, *History of St. Thomas's Hospital*, 2 v., London, Methuen, 1932-1934.

Peachey: George C. Peachey, *A Memoir of John and William Hunter*, Plymouth, England, printed for the author by William Brandon and Son, 1924.

Rush, *Autobiography*, ed. Corner: *The Autobiography of Benjamin Rush*, ed. George W. Corner, Phila., *Mem. Amer. Philos. Soc.* **25**, 1948.

Nancy Shippen, *Her Journal Book*: Same title, ed. Ethel Armes, Phila., Lippincott, 1937.

Tyerman: Rev. Luke Tyerman, *The Life of the Rev. George Whitefield*, 2 v., N. Y., 1877.

The Universal Director: The Universal Director, or The Nobleman's and Gentleman's True Guide to the Masters and Professors of the Liberal and Polite Arts and Sciences and of the Mechanic Arts, Manufactures and Trades established in London and Westminster and their Environs, London, 1763. Addresses of many figures of the period have been obtained from this volume, said to be the first business directory issued in London.

Walpole: *The Letters of Horace Walpole*, chronologically arranged and edited by Mrs. Paget Toynbee, 16 v., Oxford, Clarendon Press, 1903-1905.

Wertenbaker: T. J. Wertenbaker, *Princeton 1746-1896*, Princeton Univ. Press, 1946.

Wilks and Bettany: Samuel Wilks and A. T. Bettany, *A Biographical History of Guy's Hospital*, London, 1892.

Warwick Wroth: Warwick Wroth, *Pleasure Gardens of the Eighteenth Century*, London, 1896.

Many other volumes used in the preparation of this work may be traced through the index, which contains the names of all authors mentioned.

Introducing William Shippen, Jr.

BEFORE the start of the first medical school in this country (the medical department of the College of Philadelphia, 1765), a young physician, Dr. William Shippen, Jr., who had received his M. D. at the University of Edinburgh, was independently at work in Philadelphia giving courses of instruction in midwifery and anatomy. William Shippen, Jr., whose father was a highly esteemed physician, actively interested in the affairs of the College of New Jersey [1] and a trustee of the College of Philadelphia, had been sent abroad in 1758 to study medicine. He had immediately come under the influence of John and William Hunter in William Hunter's dissecting and lecture rooms where anatomical teaching of a remarkable order flourished. For clinical training he walked the wards of St. Thomas's Hospital and attended with special profit the midwifery courses given outside hospitals by Dr. Colin Mackenzie, well known for his skill as man-midwife. After two years in London Shippen proceeded to Scotland for his theoretical studies and graduated from the University of Edinburgh in 1761.[2] The following year he returned to America.

John and William Hunter had left their stamp upon him. What he had learned during his student days would never leave him. Other American students of the period, notably Morgan, Kuhn, and Rush, destined to become Shippen's close associates on the faculty of the first medical school in the colonies, were exposed to similar influences and responded according to individual make-up—Morgan distinguishing himself as founder of the school,

[1] For complete biographical sketch see Montgomery, 84-86. Dr. Shippen, Sr. was a member of the Continental Congress 1778, 1779, and Vice President of the American Philosophical Society, 1768. Dr. William Shippen and Robert Smith, the Philadelphia architect, had submitted a plan for Nassau Hall to the Trustees of the College of New Jersey which was adopted in 1754 (Wertenbaker, 37).

[2] Samuel Lewis, List of the American Graduates in Medicine at Edinburgh from 1705-1866 with their Theses, N. E. Hist. and Geneal. Register 42: 160, 1888.

Kuhn as faithful teacher and practitioner while the many-sided
Rush is remembered today chiefly for his humanitarian and re-
forming endeavors. Shippen, when he first came to London fresh
from the provinces at the most impressionable stage of his life,
received as it were " the laying on of hands " from the Hunters
and four years later brought back to America from this fortunate
contact the secrets of their technical methods and above all else
the spirit of their experimental approach to the problems of
human structure and of child-bearing. For a lifetime he must be
both anatomist and obstetrician.

Rush's autobiography and Morgan's ambitious journal of his
European travels while a medical student have been available to
readers previously, but nothing has been known of William Shippen's student days until a slight diary which he kept for six months
in London was discovered in the 1900's by Dr. J. Hall Pleasants
of Baltimore, in whose library it has ever since been treasured.
Dr. Pleasants found this diary when he was called upon to advise
heirs of the late Dr. Charles C. Shippen of Baltimore regarding
the disposal of their kinsman's medical library, part of which
had come from Philadelphia relatives. While examining the
volumes Dr. Pleasants caught sight of a booklet covered with
handwriting and lying on the attic floor. Upon examination this
booklet proved to be a record kept in London by William Shippen,
Jr. from July 19, 1759 to January 22, 1760. Some of the leaves
were loose and we may suppose some had been lost. Through
Dr. Pleasants' generous cooperation the contents of the diary can
now at last be published and from its pages we may learn how
an eighteenth century medical student spent his time in laboratory and hospital and how he used his leisure hours in London.
Meagre as this record is, it serves the modern reader as a psycho-
graph. Its entries, always brief and factual, develop a quickened
pace and seem to mirror from day to day the student's growing
absorption in his profession. In this sharpening of his interest,
in this change of his mood we can see foreshadowed the mature
man who will find his life's most enduring satisfaction in a long
career as successful professor in a medical school, broken only by
an interval, not altogether fortunate, as Director General of mili-

tary hospitals during the Revolution. It is with young William Shippen, Jr. that this account deals, with a young doctor in the making and his unconscious self-disclosures in a hastily kept diary. Curious, eager, athirst for knowledge, fond of excitement, fond of people, socially at ease, William Shippen, Jr. was early marked for success in a medical career. Of such stuff the best medical students are always made.

No diary of the events of his later life is known today, and apparently only one of his letters has been published. This letter,[3] written in 1784, was sent to congratulate William Cullen of Edinburgh, his former professor who always treated him with " affability and politeness," upon Cullen's " arrival at the pinnacle of medical Fame " and to introduce to his attention Mr. James Lyons, " a young gentleman of good understanding, great industry and good manners " who " cannot think himself perfected till he has received the last polish from your improving Lectures." It is a delightful letter, brief but piquant in flavor, recalling to Cullen's mind his pupil of 1761, now writing the letter, who not only had the honor to attend his lectures but who, years ago, " was as fond of Solan goose as you." Shippen refers briefly to his own academic life, his teaching of " Anatomy Surgery and Midwifery in our University, from whence we have sent out this spring 8 young gentlemen of very promising appearance as Bachelors of Medicine." He regrets that a son whom he named for William Hunter did not live, for " before this time he might have been sitting at your Feet; I have but one and he is reading Law, now 20 years old and 6 feet 2 inches high, a Boy no father need be ashamed of, but what right have I to take up your attention with these matters? "

Where are the other letters Shippen should have written if this is a fair sample of his skill? Where is his Introductory Lecture to his first anatomy course in which he is supposed to have outlined his ideas for establishment of a medical school in Philadelphia? Was he so preoccupied with his single-minded performance as pathfinder in American medical education that he had no time to write up the medical observations he could not

[3] Reprinted in *Medical Life* **32**: 137, N. Y., 1925.

avoid making during a long career of teaching? He has left no
scientific publications. Because of the paucity of material available he has had no biographer, and at this time only a sketch can
be offered of William Shippen and the world he lived in so com-
petently and intelligently that he shaped an admirable future
course for the teaching of anatomy and obstetrics in America.

Forebears, Early Life, and Education

THE pattern of William Shippen, Jr.'s mind and character was shaped by exceptionally favorable circumstances of birth, rearing and formal education. Edward Shippen, his great-grandfather, the first of the Shippens in America, well born at Methley in the West Riding of Yorkshire, England, had crossed the Atlantic to Boston in 1669 to better his fortunes, but upon marriage to a Quakeress had endured such religious persecution that eventually he had abandoned Massachusetts for the City of Brotherly Love. Philadelphia, recognizing his merits, had made him the city's first mayor in 1701. This Edward Shippen was the founder of a progressive family [1] whose marriages allied its members with many other principal figures in the colonial capital's financial, social, and professional circles. The Shippen network was spreading even into Maryland and Virginia. In Pennsylvania beyond the bounds of Philadelphia the family had an outstanding member in Edward of Lancaster (1703-1781), [2] a public-spirited merchant whose activities carried him into town planning in the "laying out" of Shippensburg and gave him a share among leading Presbyterians in the founding of the College of New Jersey later named Princeton University from the site of its final location.

Both Edward of Lancaster and his younger brother, Dr. William Shippen of Philadelphia, were prominent Presbyterian laymen, so it was natural enough that young William Shippen, Jr. should be sent to boarding school in West Nottingham where a remarkable Presbyterian clergyman, Dr. Samuel Finley, was headmaster. [3] Dr.

[1] Thomas Willing Balch, The English ancestors of the Shippen Family and Edward Shippen of Philadelphia, *Penna. Mag. Hist. Biog.* **28**: 385-402, 1904.

[2] "Edward of Lancaster," 1703-1781, was partner of the firm Logan and Shippen; later senior partner of Shippen and Lawrence; Mayor of Philadelphia, 1744; Trustee of the College of New Jersey, 1748-1767; moved to Lancaster, 1752, served as county judge under both provincial and state governments, prothonotary many years, also registrar, recorder, and clerk of Quarter Sessions Court (R. Winder Johnson, *The ancestry of Rosalie Morris Johnson*, 192, Phila., privately printed Ferris and Leach, 1905).

[3] Rush, *Autobiography*, ed. Corner, 28-33.

Finley, whose career later culminated in the presidency of Princeton, devoted many years to the training of adolescents. While his pupils lived in his country home he regarded them almost as sons. It is to Benjamin Rush, who enjoyed his tutelage a few years later, that we owe the only available account of life at the academy in West Nottingham during the colonial period. Apparently Dr. Finley was as punctilious about table manners as Latin grammar and, surprisingly enough for a clergyman of that day, placed emphasis upon farm work as well as knowledge of New Testament precepts. Country life at the school gave pupils opportunity for sports such as hunting, fishing, and riding. The course of study they pursued led naturally to continuation of intellectual application at the College of New Jersey, located at the time in Newark, where William Shippen, Jr., distinguished himself sufficiently to be chosen valedictorian of the class graduating in 1754. His Latin oration was heard among others by the Reverend George Whitefield of England who received an M. A. at the same exercises.[4] If we can trust the report of William Shippen, Jr.'s eulogist, speaking more than half a century later, the young valedictorian " attracted the eye of every beholder " by " the elegance of his person, the ease and gracefulness of his whole deportment." As his discourse proceeded his personal charms were eclipsed by his eloquence. " A power of fascination seemed to issue from his tongue."[5] His listener, George Whitefield, is said to have compared him in flowery language to the Roman orators and it was predicted that a successful career assuredly awaited him in the ministry.

The Shippen family had other plans. William Shippen, Jr., at once became his father's medical apprentice. From Shippen's hand we have no record of this period of his training. Again we must turn to the Autobiography of Benjamin Rush for a description of the duties assumed by a doctor's apprentice.[6] Rush relates that in the service of John Redman[7] from 1761 to 1766

[4] Tyerman, **2**: 334.

[5] *Port Folio*, 3rd ser. **1** (2), Feb. 1813, Shippen Eulogy.

[6] Rush, *Autobiography*, ed. Corner, 38, 39.

[7] John Redman, 1722-1808, M. D. Leyden 1748, Philadelphia's leading physician at that time. Among his distinguished pupils, in addition to Rush, were John Morgan and Caspar Wistar.

he prepared and compounded medicines, visited the sick, and performed " many little offices of a nurse to them " and in addition " took exclusive charge of his [preceptor's] books and accompts." In the intervals of business he read eagerly " at late and early hours " all available medical literature. Young Shippen's life in his father's office must have been quite similar. Possibly a father's special interest in his son's professional development may have provided opportunities for assisting in minor surgery and with obstetrical cases. Living at home as he did with his parents, two brothers, and a sister in a city where he had scores of friends and relatives, it is certain that young Shippen, unlike Rush, made social life an important part of a well organized program.

Four years of diligent service as apprentice seemed suitable preparation for a period of foreign study which was necessary at the time for all professional students with aspirations who lived in the American colonies far from established centers of learning. The elder Shippen wrote to his brother, Edward of Lancaster, in the fall of 1757 that he was " casting about to raise a sum of money for Billey's improvement abroad." [8] Somehow the money was found. Perhaps Edward of Lancaster made a contribution; at any rate by September 1 of the following year his brother wrote him a full statement of the program William, Jr., would follow while pursuing advanced medical studies across the sea: [9]

Philadelphia, 1 September, 1758

Billey goes on board Capt. Dingo's fine ship bound to Liverpool, from thence to London where he will find G. Whitefield and Mr. De Berdt, a Methodist Mercht. of great reputation as a Trader, who will direct him in regard to a Manly, Genteel frugality in his Expenses and Living—as friendly & as sincerely as well as judiciously as any man in London, and I think from his connections with them and their friends he will be despised by your Rakes and Fops whose acquaintance and commendation would be his Disgust and Ruin. He is to spend this winter in London with the finest Anatomist for Dissections, Injections, &c in England; at the same time visit the Hospitals daily, to attend Lectures of Midwifery with a Gentleman who will make that branch as familiar to him as he can want or wish to have it. In the Spring or the beginning of the Summer he goes

[8] Shippen Papers (HSP) **3**: 33. Letter of William Shippen to his brother Edward Shippen, September 2, 1757.
[9] *Ibid.*, 197.

to France through Leyden where he gets Graduated and sees all the operations of Surgery that can be performed by those Monsieurs; upon the whole he seems determined to understand surgery [so] perfectly that when he returns (If Ever) no Case can happen in his Business that he can't undertake to manage with Ease and freedom. This is inter nos—because you know our *Geese* are all *Swans*.

It is from another letter written in London six months later in March, 1759, that the first news comes to us from William Shippen, himself, about his foreign venture. Again it is a report addressed to Edward of Lancaster:

London 10th March 1759

Dear and hon'd Uncle,

After an unpleasant and dangerous voyage of 7½ weeks I arrived at Belfast in the North of Ireland. The last week I was put to an allowance of a Quart of Water per diem and Salt Meat, which much enhanced the pleasure of the Irish Shore; to avoid the pleasure of sailing more I took horse for Dublin about 120 miles from Belfast, a very fine City; in 24 hours I arrived, from hence at Park Gate,[10] very much pleased to find myself on the english Shore. I came to this little World Nov. 25th, and altho' I have been here 4 months have not seen the half of it.

I find the ways of Vice and Wickedness as many and as various as I expected; but can with pleasure and without boasting say, I find very little Difficulty shunning them; nothing necessary but a little Resolution and a constant call to more necessary Business; I now and then by accident amuse myself with Garrick's inimitable playing; by accident because Dr. Hunter's anatomical lectures begin at the same time; and I hope I shall always have the good sense to make Pleasure give way to Business. Your instructing lessons upon the frugal use of Time and Money are always in my mind and influence my conduct much.—My Father will inform you, Sir, how I spend my Time and I flatter myself to convince the World at some future day that I do not spend it trifling about Play Houses, Operas, reading idle romantic Tales or trifling Newspapers at Coffee Houses, &c, &c, as I find many have done before me, but in the right Improvement

---

[10] The port of Park Gate rose into consequence through the maintenance of " four stout packets which ply uninterruptedly back and forth between that port and Dublin " (Thomas Pennant, letter in same volume with *Literary life*, 124, London, 1793). Park Gate on the River Dee (west coast of England near Chester) must have been the place where Shippen first put foot on English soil, since the voyage from Dublin took only twenty-four hours. The development of Birkenhead as a port belongs to a later period.

of those advantages which are not to be had in my own country, which are peculiarly great in my Way of Surgery and Anatomy.—I live with the best practical Anatomist in Europe, I think I may say.—I suppose you long ago received the Copper Plate Book for Miss Burd which I sent by Capt. Nicholson about Christmas. I shall always, Sir, take pride in executing your Commands with Care and Punctuality.—My Money I think I spend very cautiously, yet as you observed, it melts faster than I imagined; nothing done in London without Pay; else how could a Million of Souls be supported?—I have had the honor of dining with the Proprietor who inquired particularly after the Shippen family and was very complaisant to me.—Mr. Hamilton intends for America in the Summer; Mr. Franklin and Son I don't know when; the Son is Barrister at Law.

The Bearer is Mr. Inglis [11] who formerly kept a school in Lancaster, has just received Orders.

Pray, Sir, present my best Congratulations to my Cousin Colonels [12] on their safe Conquest of Fort Du Quesne. [13]

I am, D^r and hon'd Uncle, with most dutiful Affections to Aunt, Kind Love to Cousin Sally and her dear little Brother, &c,

> Your dutiful Nephew
> & very humble Servt,
>
> W^m. Shippen Jr. [14]

N. B. I find as many fools in England as America and your remarks are all just.

---

[11] Charles Inglis, 1734-1816, emigrated to America when twenty-one, taught in the Free School, Lancaster, Pa., returned to England to take holy orders and was assigned in 1759 to a post in Delaware. In the colonies he rose to become assistant and later pastor at Trinity Church, New York City, but because of Loyalist sympathies left the country in 1783. In 1787 he was appointed Bishop of Nova Scotia (DNB).

[12] Joseph Shippen, 1732-1810, four years older than his cousin William, Jr., was the son of Edward of Lancaster. Graduating from Princeton in 1753 he entered the provincial army and rose to the rank of colonel, rendering distinguished service at the capture of Fort Duquesne. His brother-in-law, Colonel James Burd, who had married Sarah Shippen, was in the same engagement (R. Winder Johnson, *The ancestry of Rosalie Morris Johnson*, 194, 195, Phila., privately printed Ferris and Leach, 1905).

[13] Fort Duquesne finally fell to the English forces under General John Forbes November 25, 1758, after two months of a mounting struggle between the French aided by the Indians and the English with provincial troops. Fort Duquesne, burned to the ground on November 24, 1758, was succeeded by Fort Pitt, erected and ready to exercise its defense by January 1, 1759. The present city of Pittsburgh, named in honor of William Pitt, 1st Earl of Chatham, grew from this beginning (George Bancroft, *History of the United States*, 2: 495, N. Y., 1885).

[14] Shippen Papers (HSP), 4: 9.

Mr. [name illegible], Jr. is gone to Leyden.
Directed

> To Edward Shippen, Esqr.
>
> in
>
> Lancaster
>
> c/o Mr. Inglis

[In another hand is the annotation]

> Answer'd 9 May 1760
>   by Dr. Morgan

There is no further information readily available from the traveler until the diary begins in mid-July 1759. The diary itself is a document requiring interpretation, with its casual references and allusions to people, places, customs, and events of mid-eighteenth century England. Shippen's entries are stripped down to the bare bone of fact, as if, unconsciously, he had transferred the techniques acquired in the anatomy laboratory to his task of writing, and had made his record a clean-cut dissection of events. The study of medicine, it is clear from his pages, was becoming increasingly absorbing but he had time to enjoy the passing show of English life. He did not live in a medical vacuum, mysteriously purged of all other interests. Responding to the impact of new experiences and opportunities which residence in London offered in abundance he made an adjustment very difficult for a foreign visitor, passing through a stage of observation as an onlooker to become a participant in the activities and pastimes of his new friends and fellow-workers.

Diary of William Shippen

July 1759.

Thursday 19.* Spent in same manner as other Thursdays being taking in Day [1] at hospital Mr. Pawl [2] took off a mans leg very elegantly. Sup'd with Governor Hamilton Dr. Smith and Martin.[3]

Friday 20th. Breakfasted with Martin and gave Dr. Smith a Letter to Philadelphia.[4] Attended Dr. Smiths [5] Lecture at 2. Spent the afternoon and Evening at 3 labours and at 11 oClock a Fracture of Leg at Guys Hospital.[6]

Saturday 21st. Rose at 7½, went to Hospital at 11 and walked round the Hospital with Dr. Reeve [7] who took in thursday last, took down all remarkable cases and prescriptions. After hospital I attended Dr. Smith Lecture de Lue Venerea till 3½. Spent the afternoon and Evening at my own apartment. Supp'd about 9 went to bed about 11.

Sunday 22d. One of my most pleasant Days, heard in forenoon Mr. Read [8] good old Gentleman, Dined with my kind friend Mr. De Berdt,[9] heard Mr. Elliot [10] in the afternoon who tho a church of England Parson is obliged to turn Dissenter for want of a church. In the evening heard Mr. Kinsman [11] an excellent Preacher at Tabernacle. Supp'd upon Peas at Mr. D. About 10 went home and bedded at 11½, having spent the Day with much peace and pleasure.

Monday 23d. July. Rose at 8 being lazy. Breakfasted and

---

* Notes on the Diary are printed immediately following its text, in sequence corresponding to entries in the Diary.

went round the Hospital with Surgeon Baker [12] not being Physicians Day,[13] he performed 2 or 3 little operations. Dr. Smiths Lecture on Menses and from 2 till 4 drank Tea with Mr. Perkins,[14] and returned home about 9 after reading late York papers.

Tuesday 24. Rose at 7. Attended Drs. Reeves and Akenside [15] in their Examinations and Prescriptions of all the Patients in St. Thomas Hospital, which lasted till 1, at 2 attended Dr. Smiths Lecture upon Gout etc. till 4. Went to Peckham [16] with Mr. Latham,[17] drank Tea at Mrs. Huthwaites [18] with Miss Bradney, etc. Returned home about 9, bedded about 11.

Wednesday 25th. Rose at 7, breakfasted at 8. Spent 3 hours in looking for Dr. Taylor,[19] and visiting some particular Patients, met the Dr. at my own appartment at one. He staid with me till 5, when I went to Ranelagh [20] being last Night, 1/. Returned home at 12; there was much company, many Mobility [21] but few Nobility.

Thursday 26th. Rose at 7 breakfasted at 8 and went to Hospital at 9½. Dr. Milner [22] took in the Patients being 49, and wrote for them, Dr. Reeves wrote for the out Patients made 10 to Day 50. At one oClock with 3 of the Physicians Pupils went to the Royal College of Physicians [23] and heard Dr. Lawrence [24] read a latin oration or Treatise De Schirro et Garcinomate. Dined with Mr. DeBerdt and spent afternoon and Evening at my own appartment; bed about 10½.

Friday 27th. Rose at 7. Spent morning reading at home. Visited by Dr. Taylor went with him to coffee house and dined with him at Brymers; at 4 booted and spurr'd myself and walk'd to Peckham. Drank Tea, and after it rode with Mr. Huthwaite,[25] Miss Huth. and Miss Jeffrys [26] to Norwood and Dulwich [27] and round the country of Norwood charmed as we went with the most pleasingly diversified Prospects, of the Counties of Kent and Surrey upon one hand, and on the other Middlesex etc., behind us London and country to the north of it, upon the whole one or other of the most enchanting rides I ever had yet; about 14 miles in all; Miss Jefferys very good and agreable chatty etc. Miss Huthwaite kind. Came to Peckham at 9 walked to London in an hour, supped and went to bed much pleased tho little tired at 11 and slept very well till

Saturday 28th Morn, 8 oClock, when my Landlady called me to Breakfast, after which I dress'd for Hospital, and walked round with Dr. Akenside a very judicious kind Physician; [28] dined at home and spent the afternoon till 5; from 5 to 10 at Mr. DeBerdts. Settled accounts with him to this Day, and find myself in his Debt, 5 Guineas exclusive of Allison's Bill 33.3. [29] A fractured Scull at Guys Hospital to Day.

Sunday 29 spent at Mr. DeBerdts etc. as other Sundays. Showed Dr. Taylor the hospital and the surgeons dressing.

Monday 30th. Rose at 7½ Went thro the hospital by myself to examine the Patients; at 3 Dr. McKensie's Lecture [30] began after which I spent 2 hours in examining a dead Body [31] at Hospital, who died suddenly, his os humeri was broke just below the capsular Ligament of that Joint, his viscera sound and good. Brain supposed to be affected. Walked this Evening to Newington, [32] and played Skittles [33] an hour with Perkins who drank Tea with me. Supped and went to bed about 10½. Lobsters for supper.

Tuesday 31st. Rose about 7. Waited upon the Physicians at Hospital till 2 oClock dined and studdied at my own appartment all the afternoon and Evening; a labour at Crucifix Lane [34] this Morning, a natural presentation.

August

Wednesday August 1st 1759. Rose at 7 went to McKensies Lecture upon Generation Conception etc. Spent the Day at home and in the Evening was called to a labour but the pains were false. Went to bed about 11 oClock.

Thursday 2d. Spent the fore Part of Day as other Thursdays in taking in Patients into Hospital, at 2 rec'd Letters from Philadelphia. At 3 took coach Box and went to Enfield [1] where I spent the Evening agreably with Miss Tuller [2] at Mr. DeBerdts.

Friday 3d August. Enfield. Mr. Gibson & Lady [2] dined with us. Mrs. DeBerdt [3] and I rode out 2 hours before Breakfast. I wrote 3 or 4 orders for Mr. DeBerdt, walk'd in the afternoon to Mr. Brittons Gardens or walks potius. [2]

Saturday 4th. Rose at 7 breakfasted and took coach for the dirty London, with Mr. DeBerdt, Lady and children. At 12 saw Mr. Way [4] Surgeon to Guy's Hospital amputate a leg above the knee very dexterously 3 ligatures. 3 patients at Enfield all better, one with worms, which B. Jovial cured, one obstruct'd menses, ℞ Pil. Rufi ℥ i Sal mart. ℥ ii in Decoct. Valer. ℞ pulv. myrrh comp: better much. [5]

Sunday 5th. Breakfasted with Mr. Teaber a Tabernacle Friend. Heard Mr. Stevens preach or rather Grunt. miserable! Dined with Dr. Taylor at Mr. DeB's. and heard in the afternoon Mr. Porter a pretty preacher and handsome man much like Mr. Cummings. Evening Mr. Davis at Tabernacle. [6] Came home after supper at Mr. D.

Monday 6th. Took coach with Mr. D's Family for Enfield. Spent the Day in writing for Mr. D. The Evening at the Assembly,[7] where we had 30 brilliant Ladies not handsom in general nor yet good dancers. The Toast Miss Wilson, my Beauty Miss Luen, I danced 2 Minuets & 6 Country Dances. A very disorderly Assembly no Regularity at all. Retired about 2 oClock, to Mr. DeBerdts where

Tuesday 7th. I rose at 9 well refresh'd, dined with Self-knowing Mason,[8] etc. mounted the coach Box at 5 in the afternoon for London. Paid 1/ for my place. Went to Bed fatigued, at 11 and rose

Wednesday 8th. to go to Peckham to ride with good Mrs. Huthwaite, to Shooters Hill[9] which commands the most extensive, and variegated Prospect perhaps in England, the windings of the River Thames in the middle of so fine a Garden, if I may so say, makes the Prospect enchanting. Dined at Peckham came home in the Evening upon Mr. Pindar's Horse[10] at 2/6, when I had the great pleasure of seeing London illuminated upon the glorious News of Prince Ferdinand's Victory[11] over the french army and General Wedel's over the Russians,[12] glorious indeed! long live Prince Ferdinand etc.! Our Philadelphia Illuminations[13] done with more spirit, only 5 or 6 candles being put up against a House that has perhaps 60 or 70 Glasses. Paltry. Saw the mob break 3 Quaker's windows, etc.[14]

Thursday 9th. rose at 8. went to hospital being taking in Day. 57 were taken in by Dr. Reeve, and Mr. Baker. Walked to Peckham to dine at Mr. Huthwaites with Mr. Mrs. Miss & Master's Latham, I Hornbuckle very merry the whole Time. Miss sings to music prettily; Mast. Latham 8 years old plays well and never was taught by any Body, a natural Fidler. Got home to bed about 10, was put in mind of home much their Family being just like my own in Philadelphia.

Friday 10th. Spent the Forenoon and afternoon at my own appartment writing Letters Home and examining my Hospital Book. In the evening carried my Letters to the coffee house.[15] Went to Bed about 10.

Saturday 11th. Walked round the hospital with the Physicians as usual, dined at home, spent the afternoon reading Lewis Dispensatory.[16] Bed 11.

Sunday 12th. Spent as before at Meetings etc.

Monday 13th. Rose at 7, to my Barbors Maid who was in Labour, continued with her till 2 oClock, when I delivered her of a Daughter. Spent the remainder of the Day at home. A labour at 11, Crucifix.

Tuesday 14th. Attended the Physicians in examining and writing for all the Patients in the Hospital. Dined with my Landlady on roasted Lamb and french Beans for 6d. Spent afternoon at home.

Wednesday 15th. Rose at 7, walked the hospital with Dresser, Surgeons and see the house dressed. Dined with Mr. DeB. Went in the Evening to see the hospital. Sup'd at Mr. Sterrys and came home tired at 11 oClock.

Thursday 16th. Spent the Forenoon as other Thursdays. Dined at home at 3 oClock. Saw Mr. Paul take off a man's leg that was mashed to pieces between 2 carts.[17] Mr. Latham drank Tea with me, who gave me some Instructions on german Flute, which I begin to blow. Without any supper went to bed at 10 oClock and rose

Friday morning 17th at 7. Spent the Day till 5 P. M. in my own appartment reading Lewis Chemistry [18] and amus-

ing myself at Musick on my flute. In the Evening went to
see the famous Johnson who is the most surprizing horseman
I ever saw.[19] He first rides a single Horse standing upon
his back galloping, then 2 a foot in a Stirrup of each Horse
then takes 3 horses puts one foot on the 2 out ones holds
all 3 Bridles and gallops them all ¾ Speed, in fine he gallops
a single Horse and while he is going full gallop he dis-
mounts, i e keeps one foot in Stirrup and touches the ground
with the other etc.

Saturday Morning 18th. Took Boat for Greenwich [20]
which costs 9d. Walked from there to Eltham [21] about 3
mile with Mr. Latham to his fathers where I was highly
fed and entertained all day, dining with Mr. Mrs. & Miss
Huthwaite upon Veal and Ham, Ducks etc. very elegant,
in the afternoon drank Tea with them and some Ladies in a
coach and four, Miss Laneton among them a very sweet
good Face, very pretty too. Miss Cleves [22] worth 10,000
too etc. went to bed at 10 oClock after emptying our Bottles
and talking medically.

Sunday 19th. Rose at 8 went to Church. After it went to
Sir John Shaw's Seat [23] which Mr. Lewis was so polite as to
show me all over. There are many fine Rooms and elegantly
furnished with some fine pieces of Painting and Tapestry
etc. Dined with the Doctor, Drank Tea and sup'd at Sir
John's, charmed with fine Prospects and rural Shrubberies
contiguous to the house; Mr. Belch and Mr. Lewis kept us
drinking claret till 12 oClock when we retired and bedded,
much pleased; Mrs. & Miss Latham drank Tea with us at
Sir John's. were very polite and kind. The Dr's. Family
most like my Father's of any I have met with in England, 3
Boys and 1 spoilt Girl like Suky.[24] A very pleasant excursion indeed!

Monday 20th August. Rose at 7 breakfasted with Dr.
Latham's Family and took coach for London at 8½ where
I arrived safe at 10½ and spent the Day in examining the
Physicians Books at Hospital. At 5 oClock took coach for
Enfield, spent the Evening at Mr. Ds. and went to bed at
11 oClock.

Tuesday 21st. Rose at 6 went upon horse Back with
Mr. Burkitt,[25] Mrs. DeBerdt's Family in the Coach for Hertford [26] to see Mr. Braceys Grotto [27] very neat and elegant
indeed! (a description see in my Curiosity). Dined at Hertford 21 miles from London, at an Inn was treated by Mr.
DeBerdt as one of his Family Drank Tea at Mrs. Gatwood's
and mounted for Enfield at 5 got there at 9. Supp'd upon a
Fowl and Beans, and bedded a little tired with riding and
seeing, about 11 oClock and rose

Wednesday 22d. At 7 took a Bowl of Bread and Milk
and took coach at 8 for London 1/6 arrived at 10½ A. M.
Spent the remainder of the Day in visiting some particular
Patients in Hospital, and reading Lewis Chemistry and
Pooles physical Vade Mecum.[28] Went to Bed at 10 oClock.

Thursday 23d. Attended Dr. Akenside in taking in Patients and prescribing for them, 56 taken in. Dr. Milner
wrote for the out Patients, till one, when I walk'd with
Mr. Latham a worthy Lad who is a Pupil at Guys, to Peckham dined at Mr. Huthwaite and drank Tea and spent the
afternoon at the Fair [29] with Miss Jeffreys in a room front-
ing the Fair, we were in Company 15, amongst the rest
was Miss Watson a very pretty young Lady mere Beauty,
Miss Sweet, Still Huthwaite, Matt. etc. etc.; Mr. L. played
upon Flute Miss Jeffreys and I sung. We danced all minuets
and in short spent the afternoon as merrily as you please.
We see the Ladies all home about 8 and then walk'd to

London 2 miles. Went to bed about 11 after reading an hour.

Friday 24th. Rose at 7 spent the Morning reading and writing, dined with Dr. Taylor, drank Tea at Dr. Shaws [30] with Mr. Latham etc. Spent the Evening at home reading, went to Bed at 11 oC.

Saturday 25th. Rose at 7. Attended Physicians walking around the Hospital till 12½ then saw Mr. Way and Paul couch 2 men in old way by depression.[31] At one oClock I bled Mrs. DeBerdt with credit. Dined with her wrote a long Letter to Suky in the afternoon drank Tea and in Evening went to hear Mr. Whitefield at Tabernacle, came home to Bed at 10.

Sunday 26th. Rose at 7½ and spent the Day as other Sundays at Mr. DeBerdts etc. Heard Mr. Godding [32] and Mr. Whitefield.

Monday 27th. Rose at 7 breakfasted with Dr. Fothergil [33] who was very familiar and sociable; paid Governour Hamilton a visit sat an hour & 1/2 with him talking over the affairs of the province etc. very polite and affable. At 11½ oClock I saw Mr. Cowel [34] cut 3 for the stone very well. At half after 12 went to Dr. McKensie's touching Lecture [35] and examined 17 pregnant women etc. Dined at 2½, at 3 went to see Dr. Taylor who is sick. Drank Tea with Mrs. Norkitt whose husband is Brother to Glover Hunts wife.[36] Spent the Evening at home.

Tuesday 28th. Rose at 7 attended the Physicians at Hospital till 1 oClock. Spent the afternoon at home.

Wednesday 29th. Rose at 6 to a Labour which lasted till night. At 8 attended Dr. McKensie, spent from 10 till 1 at my own appartment now and then visiting the Woman in Labour.   Spent afternoon and Evening till 5 in morning at Labour.

Thursday 29th.   Rose at 11 spent the Day till 4 at home. Went to White Conduit House [37] and staid till 7 came home and read till 11 went to bed and rose

September

Friday Sept. 1st. at 8.   Spent the Morning reading Lewis Chemistry till 12.   Spent an hour at Hospital.   Drank Tea with Dr. Taylor and spent the Evening at home writing and reading till 1/2 past 10 oClock.

Saturday 31st.   Walked round the Hospital with the Physicians till 1 1/2.   Dined and in the afternoon at 5 took coach for Woodford [1] 8 miles from London Easterly, came to Mr. Mitchells who was confined to his Bed with the Gout.   Mrs. Mitchel [2] and her daughter entertain'd us very well then Mr. Latham and myself play'd cards till 11½ bedded. This morning I waited upon Mr. Hamilton but too late.

Sunday September 2d.   Have mistook a Day in my calculation.   Rose at 8, went to hear Mr. Antuon and spent the remainder seeing Woodford which is situated on an Eminence commands very extensive Prospects; afternoon very wet was obliged to spend the Evening within hearing Miss read etc.

Monday 3d.   Rose at 6 walked 2 mile to Wansted [3] to see Lord Tinley's Seat which is a Mere pallace fitter for a King than nobleman.   Has before it a grand lawn beset with Marble Images and Lamps at the End of it a piece of water 11 Acres.   On one side a fine woody Grove with a great Stream of Water running thro it etc. very pretty.

Breakfasted at 9. Rode 11 Miles in Chariot,[4] to Chigwell [5] where you have the most extensive and beautifully diversified Prospect imaginable; fine Meadow imprimis with a pretty River meandering thro it in a very serpentine Manner then Groves, Valleys, Mountains, Cities, London etc. etc. Squire Crockets very elegant and pretty. Dined at 3, play'd a Tune on the Flute and sung a Song at 5 took Coach for London where we met a very agreable Company, a Parson, an old Lady, a young married Lady and a young Lady. They were much pleased and surprized at my Story of America etc. we came to London about 7. At 10 went to bed a little fatigued with Pleasure.

Tuesday 4th. Spent at Hospital till 1 oClock being Physicians Day, Dr. Taylor drank Tea with me went to see the humours of Bartholomew Fair [6] which are very vile and ridiculous. Bed at 11.

Wednesday 5th. Examined particulars in Hospital several small pox 3 out of 4 die, Saw Mr. Baker perform 3 operations, a Leg, Breast & Tumor from Girl's lower Jaw inside, very well operated. Mr. Warner extracted a large Stone from Urethra of a man and pinn'd the Incision up as in Harelip.[7] Dress'd in afternoon for Camberwell Assembly where were 40 young Ladies most of them pretty and genteel, elegantly dress'd in flounced Trollopes.[8] I danced with Miss Jeffery of Peckham, went to Bed in Camberwell [9] about 4 slep't till 9.

Thursday morning 6th. Breakfasted and came to London about 11. Spent the remainder of the Day at home and at Hospital. To bed about 9. No proper Decorum or Regularity in Assembly some sitting down as soon as they have danced to the Bottom; very fine were Miss Innocent, Watsons, Seatons, Jepson, Coit and Thomas etc.[10]

Friday 7th. At home and visiting 4 or 5 patients in Small-pox etc.[11] In the Evening went to see City illuminated etc. Went to bed at 11 oClock.

Saturday 8th. Rose at 7 read Warners Chirurgical Cases [12] till 11, dress'd and went to Hospital as other Saturdays; heard Mr. Whitefield preach in the Evening.

Sunday 9th. Breakfasted with Mr. Teaber, went with him to hear Mr. Lawson a Scotch Presbyterian, much like Mr. Alison.[13] Dined with Mr. DeBerdt and heard Mr. Edwards a lively little Preacher, in the Evening heard Mr. Adams at Tabernacle a zealous warm loud preacher.[14] Supp'd at Mr. D. and got home at 11.

Monday 10th. Spent the forenoon at home reading Warner's Cases and Lewis Chemistry. Dined with Ralph Ashton who is just come from Scotland graduated at St. Andrews with Glentworth.[15] Spent the afternoon at home, at 7 went to a dance in the Borrough and danced with Miss S. Church a very pretty soft agreable Girl. We were very merry till 3 next morning. Went to bed at 5 slept till 1 oClock Tuesday afternoon.

Tuesday 11th. Spent the afternoon reading Warner. Tuesday evening 2 Labours at Weed Yard.[16]

Wednesday 12. Rose at 7 went to Dr. McKensie's Lecture; spent the forenoon after that showing a Gentleman Mr. Hunter anatomical curiosity [17] and afternoon and Evening with Mr. Bishop and Sterry.

Thursday 13. Dr. McKensie in morning till 9½ then taking in at Hospital till 1 oClock. Dress'd for Sadler's Hall feast and Ball,[18] dined upon fine venison etc. etc. Danced in the Evening with Miss Huthwaite and Miss Spencer, till 12, then retired home much pleased; and slept till 8 oClock. 40 Ladies.

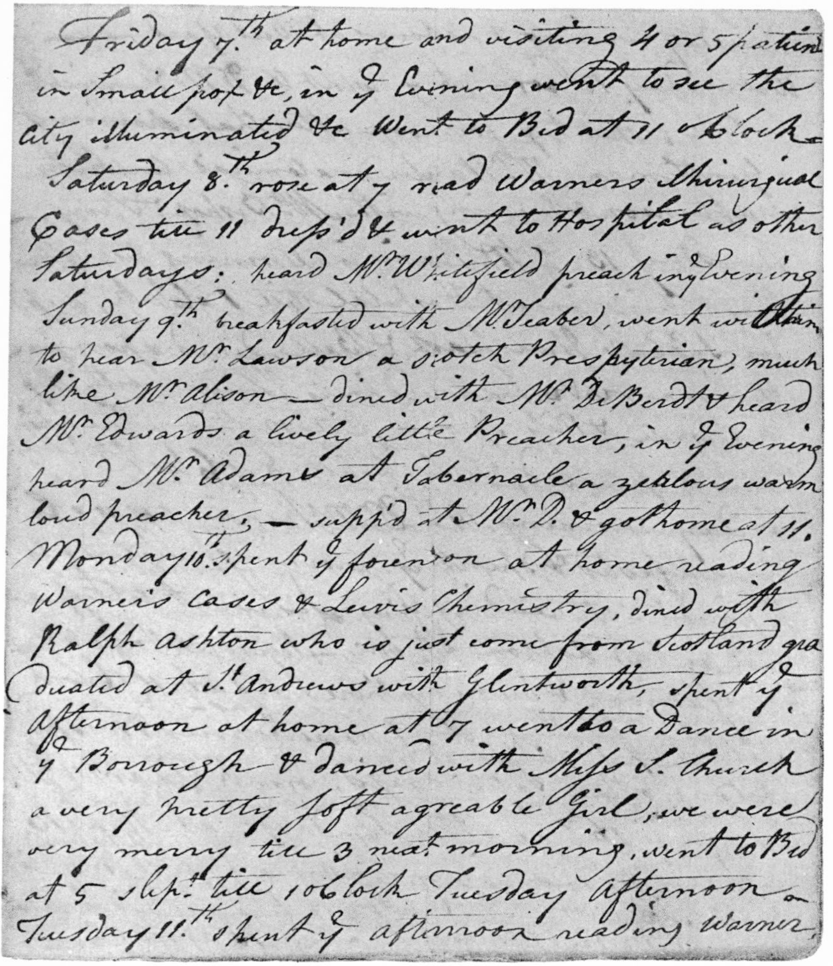

Friday 7th at home and visiting 4 or 5 patients
in Small pox &c, in ye Evening went to see the
City illuminated &c Went to Bed at 11 oClock
Saturday 8th rose at 7 read Warners Chirurgical
Cases till 11 dress'd & went to Hospital as other
Saturdays: heard Mr Whitefield preach in ye Evening
Sunday 9th breakfasted with Mr Teaber, went with them
to hear Mr Lawson a Scotch Presbyterian, much
like Mr Alison — dined with Mr DeBerdt & heard
Mr Edwards a lively little Preacher, in ye Evening
heard Mr Adams at Tabernacle a zealous warm
loud preacher, — supp'd at Mr D. & got home at 11.
Monday 10th spent ye forenoon at home reading
Warners cases & Lewis Chemistry, dined with
Ralph Ashton who is just come from Scotland gra
duated at St Andrews with Glentworth, spent ye
Afternoon at home at 7 went to a Dance in
ye Borough & danced with Miss S. Church
a very pretty soft agreable Girl, we were
very merry till 3 next morning, went to Bed
at 5 slept till 10 oClock Tuesday Afternoon —
Tuesday 11th spent ye afternoon reading Warner

Fig. 1. A page from Shippen's Diary.

Fig. 2. Covent Garden in 1751.

Friday Morning 14th. Dr. McKensie till 10 oClock. Breakfasted and spent the morning writing to Philadelphia and reading Warner. Went to Coffeehouse with Ashton [19] at one. Dined at home and spent the afternoon and Evening there. Bed at 11 oClock.

Saturday 15th. Spent at Mackensies and Hospital as other Saturdays. Drank Tea at Mr. D.

Sunday 16th. As other Sundays at Mr. De B. Heard Mr. Read in morning a grave sensible man. Afternoon Mr. Condor a scholar and bad preacher.[20] Evening Mr. White-field always agreeable.

Monday 17th. Examined some patients in small Pox. At 12 went to touching Lecture at McKensie till 2. Spent the afternoon and Evening reading etc.

Tuesday 18th. Dr. McKensie in morning. Hospital from 10 till 1 oClock dined; and at 4½ waited upon Dr. Milner with 3 other Physicians Pupils. The Dr. entertained us very agreably till 7 showing us several experiments in Electricity particularly a Stone called by the moors Treep, french Tourmalin,[21] and by the dutch Asshantrechar, which is possessed of both a negative and possitive electric power, one on one side and the other on the other side of the same Stone; we drank Tea with the Dr.

Wednesday 19. Dr. McKensie in morning; visited 3 or 4 patients in Hospital with Small pox; dined on board Capt. Blair,[22] spent the afternoon and Evening attending 2 labours difficult. Bedded at 11 after a Turn in Borough Fair.[23]

Thursday 20th. Dr. McKensie imprimis. Hospital as usual till 1 oClock, afternoon at Mr. Bishops a clergyman till 10 oClock, came home and went to bed.

Friday 21st. Dr. M. imprimis. The forenoon at home

and afternoon at Borough Fair very foolish. Evening a Labour at Crucifix Lane till 9 oC.

Saturday 22d. As other Saturdays. Dined with Mr. DeBerdt on a Hare etc.

Sunday 23d. Spent the forenoon reading Herveys D.[24] Dined as usual at Mr. Ds. heard Dr. Guyse [25] and Mr. Elliot.

Monday 24. Dr. McKensie imprimis Hospital afterwards to see 7 Small pox patients and 2 cut for the Stone by Mr. Baker; dined with Dr. Ashton, Mr. Perkins drank Tea with me; supp'd with Mr. Alexander.[26]

Tuesday 25th. Dr. M. as before. Hospital as other Tuesdays till 1 oClock. Labour at Crucifix this Morning which lasted till 2 oClock P. M. natural. Dined and spent the Day and Night at home reading and writing till 10 oClock.

Wednesday 26th. Dr. McK. imprimis went to the hospital seeing 6 Small pox patients 2 died today, confluent. Came home to dinner, instead of going to the feast where all the young Boobys belonging to the 2 Hospitals are. Went to see Garrick in the character of Archer very well.[27]

Thursday 27. Dr. McKensie and Hospital as usual. Spent the remainder of the Day at Home. Bed at 11 oClock.

Friday 28th. Dr. M. till 10 then took Coach for Enfield where I found Miss DeBerdt [28] down with small pox a good sort and few 100 in face. Mrs. DeBerdt insisted upon my staying till monday when I came to London having spent this day Saturday. Sunday I heard Mr. Howel [29] preach; found my patients much better, got an addition to the Number. Saw Miss Britton [30] a very angellic Figure! Drank Tea with Miss Palmer and Mrs. Ginks and Daughter and Miss Twitchit, very agreable.

October

Monday October 1st. Came to London about 11. Busy in packing my things for Mr. Hunter's.[1] In the Evening attended Dr. Hunter's first Lecture [2] sup'd at Robin Hood.[3]

Tuesday 2d. Dr. McK. Moved my trunk to Mr. Hunter's attended Hospital till 2. Dined. Dr. Hunter's Lecture at 5 till 7½ went to the Play to see Tom in Conscious Lovers by Mr. King from Dublin.[4]

Wednesday 3d. Set off at 7 for Enfield to see Miss DeBerdt in small pox found them turned favourably. Dined there and came to London at 5 for Dr. Hunter's Lecture lay for the first Night at Mr. Hunter's.

Thursday 4th. Rose at 7½. Dined with Dr. Reeve who has a notable Lady and 4 fine Daughters, is kind. 5 Lecture till 7. Went to Drury Lane to see Osmyn in the Mourning Bride,[5] well done indeed. Paid 1/ for Upper Gallery.[6] bed at 10½.

Friday 5th. Rose at 7 breakfasted at 8½. Dissected till Dinner and after dinner till Lecture Time 5.

Saturday October 6th. Rose at 7. Spent the Day in the dissecting room till 5 Dr's. Lecture till 7½; bed at 10½ talking Anatomy with Mr. H. from supper.

Sunday 7th. Dissected all day till 6 walk'd in the Park till 8 supped at 9 bedded at 10.

Monday 8th. Rose at 7 dissected 7 hours, till Lecture Time at 5, after Lecture operated till 9 Supper Time under the direction of Mr. Hunter.

Tuesday 9th. Rose at 6 operated till 8, breakfasted till 9, dissected till 2, dined till 3, dissected till 5. Lecture till 7, operated till 9, sup'd till 10 then bed.

Wednesday 10th. Rose at 6 and spent the Day as yesterday till 7 at night. Went to Coffeehouse till 9.

Thursday 11th. Rose at 8 dissected till 4 excluding Meals. At 5 Dr. Hunters Lecture till 7. Went to play.

Friday 12th. Dissected till 5 went to see Garrick in the character of Macbeth.[7] Surprising!

Saturday 13th. Dissected till 1. Went to coffee H. where to my great Joy, I found a Pacquet from Philadelphia. Dined with Mr. DeBerdt, attended Dr. H. Lecture at 5 till 7½, talked over Anatomy and the Lecture till 10 with Mr. Hunter.

Sunday 14th. Rose at 6 dissected till 8, breakfasted, dissected till 1, dined and dissected till 6, wrote till 11.

Monday 15. Rose at 6, dissected till 12, went with Mr. Hunter to Dr. Middleton's Auction,[8] Lecture at 5, read Sydenham [9] and chirurgical Lectures till 10.

Tuesday 16th. Dissected till 5 Lecture till 7½. Chatted till 10 with Mr. Hunter upon anatomical points bedded at 10½.

Wednesday 17th. Rose at 7 dissected till 5, lecture till 7 half a play fatal Marriage [10] with C. Blair.[11]

Thursday 18th. Pleased with the news of taking Quebec [12] Illuminations etc. Dissected till 9. Went to the Hospital at 10 till 1 to College of Physicians at 2 to hear Dr. Akenside's Oration on the immortal Harvey,[13] very entertaining. Lecture at 5 till 7½. Bed at 10.

Friday 19th. Went to Auction of Dr. Middleton and laid out £ 3: 4: 6 for books. Met Jo Mathers went to the play with him he lay with me.[14]

Saturday 20th. Dissected till 10, went for my books, and to coffee H. with Mathers. 5 oClock Lecture.

Sunday 21st. Was called up at 4 to Mrs. Allison my Taylor's wife in Labour, continued with her till 12 when I lay'd her of a fine Girl. Dined at home, went to Tabernacle in Evening with J. Mathers, heard Mr. White.

Monday 22d. Dissected till 2. Spent the Evening at home with Mr. Hunter and slep with him.

Tuesday 23d. Went to the Hospital saw a cancerous Breast and Lip extirpated by Mr. Warner, rec'd a Letter from Glasgow. Lecture at 5 as usual.

Wednesday 24th. Rose at 7 injected all Day. Lecture at 5 till 7½ went to see Mrs. Allison.

Thursday 25th. At home all Day dissecting and injecting. Lecture at 5 till 7, read Pott on the Fistula Lachrymalis [15] till 11 bed.

Friday 26th. Rose at 7 busy in anatomical room till 5 Lecture till 7½ read Douglass on hydrocele [16] till 10½ to bed.

Saturday 27th. Rose at 7 making Preparations of Gutts etc. till Lecture etc. read till 10.

Sunday 28th. Spent at Mr. DeBerdts, heard Mr. White-field in Evening and sup'd with him.

Monday 29th. Dissected till 5 Lecture till 7, went to the Play called the Confederacy [17] at D. Lane.

Tuesday 30th. Rose at 8 dissected till 5 as usual.

Wednesday 31st. Rose at 7, breakfasted with Mr. Drinker [18] and Mather. Dined with Mr. DeBerdt, Lecture at 5 till 8 read till 10.

November

Thursday November 1st. Rose at 8 busy in dissecting room all Day Lecture at Night.

Friday 2d. Went to Georges Hospital and saw Hawkins and Bromfield operate, Stone and amputation.[1] Mr. Hunter in afternoon dissecting for Glands and Ducts for Saliva. Lecture at 5 till 8. New farce High Life below Stairs[2] very good and apropos to times.

Saturday 3d. Rose at 8 saw Mr. H. extract a Steatomatous Tumor from upper Eyelid. busy in opening a Live Dog to see the Lacteals and thoracic Duct etc.[3] Lecture from 5 till 8.

Sunday 4th. as usual at Mr. DeBerdts.

Monday 5th. Dissecting all Day. Lecture till 8.

Tuesday 6th. looking at Mr. Hunter dissecting for Lecture the Muscles of Thigh and Leg. Lecture at 5. At Roberts till 9, sup'd and bed.

Wednesday 7th. Rose at 7. Mr. Hunter dissecting Muscles for Lecture. Went to see a patient under my care. Oyl. After Lecture went to Bartholomews Hospital[4] and saw the neatest operation for Bubonocele that I ever saw by Mr. Pott a very clever neat Surgeon.[5] Home at 9.

Thursday 8th. Rose at 7 waited upon Mr. Franklin at 10. Dined with him and Messrs. Sanson and Sweat[6] at his House Lecture as usual.

Friday 9th. Spent all the Day at Lord Mayor's Show and Ball[7] at night after Lecture till 3. Slept with Mr. Teaber.

Saturday 10th. Spent the Day till Dinner Time with Messrs. Wikoff[8] and Clarkson[9] and came to Lecture at 5. Saw G. in K. Lear inimitable.[10]

Sunday 11th. Dissected till 1 oClock went to Mr. De-Berdts and found Wikoff and Clarkson unwell. Tabernacle in Evening with C.

Monday 12th. Dissected till 2, on an Arm. Lecture at 5 till 7½ went to coffeehouse and to see Mr. Wikoff found him brave again.

Tuesday 13th. Dissected till 3. Went to Park and Play [11] with Clarkson he slept with me.

Wednesday 14th. Dissected till 11. Went to see St. Pauls, whispering Gallery etc. etc. till 2. Dined and Lecture at 5 as usual.

Thursday 15th. Hospital in Morning, din'd with Mr. Wikoff at Mr. D. he came home with me lay with me, he went to play, I to Lecture, Garrick in Lear.

Friday 16th. Shew'd him the park etc etc. Dissected all the remainder of the Day. Lecture at 5 till 8. Talk'd anatomically with J. Hunter, bed at 10.

Saturday 17th. Dissected till 5 Lecture as usual. Bed at 10.

Sunday 18th. Wrote Letters till 12. Spent the remainder of Day at Mr. DeBerdts as usual.

Monday 19th. Dissected till 12 went to coffehouse to see Budden,[12] not there. Lecture at 5.

Tuesday 20th. Dissected all Day. Lecture at 5 till 7½. Went to see half of A Woman's a Riddle.[13]

Wednesday 21st. Dissected till Lecture at 5 till 7½. Spent the Evening with a young Lady.

Thursday 22nd. Spent the Day on Board Capt. Budden and getting the apples etc. on Shore. Lecture at 5 till 7½.

Friday 23d. Dissected till 5. Lecture till 7½. Went to see Comus [14] and hear a new Singer; bed at 11.

Saturday 24th. Dissected all Day. Lecture as usual. Spent the Evening at home merrily till 11.

Sunday 25th. Spent at Mr. DeBerdts and Tabernacle with Mr. Wikoff. Waited upon Mr. Ewer [15] in Evening.

Monday 26th. Dissected all Day. Lecture as usual. Spent Evening at Roberts with 3 or 4 friends.

Tuesday 27th. Dissected till 4. Received Letters from home by Mr. Ewer; Lecture at 5. Clarkson slept with me.

Wednesday 28th. Dissected all Day Lecture at 5.

Thursday 29th. Thanksgiving Day,[16] spent at Mr. De-Berdts heard Mr. Whitefield in the Evening.

Friday 30th. Dissected all Day. Evening Lecture etc.

December

Saturday December 1st. Injected 2 hearts till Dinner. Spent the Evening at Drury Lane.[1] No Lecture.

Sunday 2d. Spent the Day at Mr. De Berdts as customary heard Mr. Elliot in Evening.

Monday 3d. Dissected all Day Lecture in Evening.

Tuesday 4th. Spent the Day in City with Mr. Clarkson. Lecture in Evening. Bed at 11.

Wednesday 5th. Dissected all Day Lecture in Evening.

Thursday 6th. Spent the Day in taking down proportions for Injections [2] from Mr. Hunter and being no Lecture in Evening went to see the Play of Oroonoko [3] where Garrick and Mrs. Cibber [4] are excellent.

Friday 7th. Dissected and Lecture as usual.

Saturday 8th. inject 2 hearts and dissected them. Evening Lecture upon the heart.

Sunday 9th. Spent at Mr. DeBerdts and hearing Mr. Whitefield with Mr. Clarkson supp'd upon Philadelphia cranberry Pye very fine.[5]

Monday 10th. Dissected an Arm. Attended Lecture from 5 till 7. Spent Evening at Miss Caswells.

Tuesday 11th. Dissected all Day. Lecture in Evening.

Wednesday 12th. Attended Mr. Hunter in proportioning injecting Ingredients and taking them down; Lecture as usual from 5 till 7½. Diverted myself with a 1/ worth of a play, and a new farce Love a la Mode very diverting indeed and well acted.[6]

Thursday 13th. Waited upon Mr. Hunter while he injected a Body for blood Vessels; Lecture in the Evening till 8. Supd at 9 bed at 10.

Friday 14th. Injected myself a Child for the peculiarity of Foetus and a head of another. Lecture as usual and in Evening a new foolish farce Tutor.[7]

Saturday 15. Spent in City. Dined with Mr. Huthwaite. Lecture as usual in Evening till 8.

Sunday 16th. Spent the Forenoon at Home reading. Dined at 4½ with Mr. Propr. Penn and my Lady Juliana, Miss Frame etc. very polite and agreable, etc.[8]

Monday 17th. Injected another child and busy in preparing things to be sent by Capt. McClelland.[9]

Tuesday 18th. Dissected all Day. Lecture at 4. Went to a Ball in City after Lecture, danced with Miss Knox an agreable Lady and good Dancer. 35 Ladies genteely dress'd etc. Bed at 2.

Wednesday 19th. Injected a Body etc. all Day. Lecture from 5 to 7 ¾. Went to a Play Refusal [10] at Drury Lane for 1/. Bed at 11.

Thursday 20th. Busy all day making Preparations of thoracic Duct, etc. Lecture as usual.

Friday 21st. Busy in Injecting Room. Dined at 1. Attended Lecture at 5. Went to see 1/2 a play. [11]

Saturday 22d. Spent as the Day before. Evening at home with Mr. Hunter who generally lies out of town.

Sunday 23d. Terrified at 4 oClock with a Fire very nigh in Kings Street 30 houses burnt; [12] the rest at Mr. DeBerdts.

Monday 24th. In Preparation Room all Day. Lecture as usual. Spent an hour at Roberts Coffeehouse.

Tuesday 25 Christmas Day. Went to St. James's to see the Royal Family go to Chappell, [13] with Clarkson. Dined upon Mincepyes etc. at home, went in the afternoon to Chelsea College [14] and see all the Curiosity of it, went to Coffeehouse R. sup'd at 9. Spent 2 hours at Derrys.

Wednesday 26th. Preparing a head etc. till 3 oClock when double Lectures began at 3 and 6 2 hours each finishing at 8½. Drank a dish of coffee and supp'd at 10.

Thursday 27th. Went to Hospital Dr. Akenside taking in Coffee House afterward. Dined in City with Dr. Clarkson at Cock. [15] Lecture at 3 and 6.

Friday 28th. Breakfasted at 8 busy in Preparation Room till Dinner. Lecture as before.

Saturday 29th. Waited upon Cousin Sterling [16] was very much pleased to see her and she me. Dined at home lecture as usual.

Sunday 30th. Cousin Sterling not well Mr. Willing [17] called upon me to go and see her, bled her and bled Miss DeBerdt [18] too who was unwell. Dined at Mr. DeBerdts. Heard famous Mr. Edwards [19] preach etc.

Monday 31st. Spent the Day in the preparing Room. Evening with Clarkson, Francis [20] etc. My patients much better.

January, 1760

Tuesday 1st January 1760. Dined with Mr. DeBerdt tho invited to dine with Mr. J. Ewer.[1] Spent the Evening with some Pennsylvania Friends jovially.

Wednesday 2. Busy at home till 1. Dined with Mr. Aufrere [2] by Mr. Francis recommendation. His Lady the most sensible agreable woman I ever saw, she entertained us with an acct. of Mr. Pitts Speech in the House of Commons when he spoke of Quebec's being taken and lamented the Death of the brave G. Wolf [3] . . . most charming woman indeed! Sup'd at Covent Garden with Mr. Francis and Clarkson. Bed at 12. Miss Aufrere of 7 Years a wonderful Girl.[4]

Thursday 3rd. Busy all Day dissecting etc. Lectures finishd.

Friday 4th. Busy in the same Manner. Went to a play in Evening with T. Francis.[5] Bed at 11.

Saturday 5th. Rose at 9 dissected until 1½. Dined and [page torn]. . . . Time spent in visiting Friends etc. a violent . . . Dissection and preparation entirely, visited . . . often who is very hearty. Dined with Francis . . . Capt. Budden and Bolitho [6] too. Thursday last went to the Royal Society with . . . Franklin [7] etc. twelfth Night went to Court with

. . . klin and saw the Royal family,[8] and the greatest and best . . . Mob [9] I ever saw. Lasted till 2 lost my Hat and. . . .

Monday 14th January. Lectures began; busy in. . . . Lectures all Day. Lecture in Evening from 5 to 7½.

Tuesday 15th. Busy'd in the same Manner. Lecture in Evening.

Wednesday 16th. Writing all Day till Lecture.

Thursday 17. Writing all Day Lecture in Evening. ½ a play to see Garrick in Ranger.[10]

Friday 18 went to see Mrs. Sterling in the City then to the Coffee House. Dined with W. Franklin [11] and D. Clarkson. Lecture at 5 till 7½.

Saturday 19th. Performing operations all Day . . . ure in Evening as usual. Went to see Comus at C. G.[12]

Sunday 20. Spent with Mrs. Sterling and at Mr. De-Berdts. Heard the famous Fordyce an affected stiff orator.[13]

Monday 21st. Cleaning and making preparations . . . preparation Room. Writing all the Even. . . .

Tuesday 22. Performed 3 or 4 operations. Went. . . . Dined with T. Francis, Capt. Budden, Bolitho, etc. . . . from home. Lecture in Evening after it. . . .

NOTES TO DIARY OF WILLIAM SHIPPEN

July, 1759

[1] Patients were admitted to St. Thomas's Hospital, Southwark, every Thursday (Parsons, **2**: 217).

[2] Joseph Paul, surgeon to St. Thomas's 1741-1760 (*ibid.*, 201, 218).

[3] This supper party seems to have been a gathering of visitors from America. James Hamilton, *ca.* 1710-1783, acting Governor of Pennsylvania 1748-1754, 1759-1763, 1771, 1773, was in London at this time on provincial business. The Reverend William Smith, 1727-1803, Provost of the new College of Philadelphia, had arrived in London New Year's Day 1759. In March he had been honored with the degree D. S. T. by both Aberdeen and Oxford (Montgomery, 332, 344). Martin may well have been a young student from America, possibly Josiah Martin of Long Island, in whose family as a young Scottish tutor William Smith had first reached the American colonies in 1751. Josiah Martin was at the Temple studying law about this time and had been granted an honorary A. B. *in absentia* by the College of Philadelphia at its first Commencement, May 17, 1757 (*ibid.*, 186, 286; *London Chronicle*, October 15-18, 1757).

[4] Letters from England to Philadelphia took seven or eight weeks in transit. Entrusted to the hands of a special messenger, safe delivery was better assured. Any letters sent home by WS at this time reached their destination October 8, 1759, the day of Dr. William Smith's return to Philadelphia (Montgomery, 344).

[5] Two Smiths seem entangled here in this hasty record. Undoubtedly WS was attending in the next few days a series of lectures by a medical man and not by a theologian. The lecturer was probably Dr. Hugh Smith, an Edinburgh graduate in medicine, 1755, who came to London 1759 and gave lectures at Middlesex Hospital soon after (DNB).

[6] Guy's Hospital bears the name of Thomas Guy, bookseller, *ca.* 1644-1724, who left his fortune for its establishment (DNB).

[7] Thomas Reeve, physician to St. Thomas's 1740-1760 (Parsons **2**: 263; see p. 55).

[8] Possibly Henry Reed, whose sermons were being printed 1729-1755 (BB).

[9] Dennys De Berdt of the firm of De Berdt and Burkitt, North America Merchants, Artillery Court, Chiswell Street is listed in *The Universal Director*, London, 1763. Descendant of Huguenot refugees he was prominent among dissenters and known for his friendliness to the American colonies. He had served in advisory capacity to Delaware and in 1765 he was elected colonial agent for Massachusetts. His portrait now hangs in the Massachusetts State House, Boston (DAB).

[10] Probably the Reverend Richard Elliott of Benet College, Cambridge (d. 1778), who sometimes assisted in services at the residence of the Countess of Huntingdon in Portland Row, Cavendish Square. His sermon: *Grace and Truth, or a Summary of Gospel Doctrine, considered in A Funeral Sermon on the Death of the Rev. George Whitefield* was published in London 1770 (BB; Tyerman, **2**: 558, 621).

[11] Andrew Kinsman, 1725-1793, often addressed by Whitefield as his "dear Timothy," had been violently persecuted for his support of his leader's cause. Kinsman, who attributed his conversion to reading Whitefield's sermons, became an itinerant preacher of note and was finally ordained pastor at Plymouth Docks (Tyerman, **2**: 216 *n.*).

[12] Thomas Baker, surgeon to St. Thomas's 1739-1768 (Parsons, **2**: 265).

[13] Tuesday was Physician's Day at St. Thomas's (*ibid.*, **2**: 217).

[14] Mr. Perkins, unidentified, was perhaps a fellow student. Whenever possible

persons and places referred to in the Diary have been identified in the notes. Otherwise, no information could be found.

[15] Mark Akenside, 1721-1770, was appointed physician to St. Thomas's in 1759. Poet as well as physician, his *Pleasures of the Imagination* had attracted much notice upon publication when he was only twenty-three. He had received his medical degree from Leyden the same year (DNB).

[16] Peckham, now part of greater London, was in 1759 "a pleasant village in Surrey and a hamlet of Camberwell where tradesmen and those who have retired from business live in attractive villas and neat houses of retirement" (*The Ambulator*).

[17] John Latham, 1740-1837, became more distinguished as an ornithologist than as a physician (DNB).

[18] See p. 15.

[19] Dr. Taylor remains a mystery. Since his first visit to WS lasted four hours they must have been friends previously. During the summer they had other social contacts. One Sunday they spent with the De Berdts, on another Dr. Taylor was shown the hospital. When he became ill WS dutifully visited him. After September 1 Dr. Taylor disappears from the diary and we may venture the guess that he returned either to America or to some English provincial town.

[20] Ranelagh, well known place of entertainment, rivaling New Spring Gardens (Vauxhall) with the resources of its vast Rotunda. Ranelagh's extensive gardens opened annually in April while the Houses of Parliament were sitting and its entertainments ended in July, by which time most people of rank had retired to the country. Admission, usually 2 s. 6 d., was reduced to a shilling on certain evenings (Austin Dobson, 2: 263-283; Warwick Wroth, 199-212).

[21] *Mobility* was a word in good usage in the eighteenth century to denote the mob. WS uses it here to describe the crowd of ordinary citizens he saw in late July at Ranelagh (OED; Fielding's *Covent Garden Journal*, ed. Jensen, 2(49): 34).

[22] Thomas Milner, physician to St. Thomas's 1759-1762. Resignation from the hospital staff after a few years usually meant that a man had acquired so extensive a private practice that he was forced to give up his hospital connection (Parsons, 2: 220).

[23] Thomas Pennant describes the College of Physicians, Warwick Lane, the work of Christopher Wren: "On the top of the dome is a gilt ball which the witty Garth calls the gilded pill; on the summit of the centre is the bird of Aesculapius, the admonishing cock" (Thomas Pennant, *Some account of London*, 372, London, 1793).

[24] Thomas Lawrence's lecture, *De Schirro et carcinomatate*, must have been one of his Croonian lectures which he gave in 1758 and 1759 under terms of the foundation established by the will of Dr. Croone, fellow of RCP, who died in 1694 (Munk's *Roll*, 3: 359). Dr. Lawrence, 1711-1783, well versed in classics, always corresponded in Latin with his friend and patient, Dr. Johnson, about the latter's ailments. Johnson described Lawrence as "a learned, intelligent communicative companion . . . one of the best men I have known" (Boswell's *Johnson*, ed. Ingpen, 2: 974).

[25] Mr. Huthwaite may have been a chemist, member of the firm Huthwaite and Company, Wood Street, Cheapside. *The Universal Director* lists this firm under chemists, with the heading "the following are really artists having regular laboratories of their own."

[26] Since *The Ambulator* reports that tradesmen flocked to Peckham, Miss Jefferys may have been a daughter of Thomas Jefferys listed by *The Universal Director* as Engraver and Geographer to his Majesty in the Strand, Corner of St. Margaret's Lane.

[27] Norwood, "a village five miles from London in the parish of Croydon, Surrey. It bears no marks of its vicinity to the capital and those who love the contemplation of unimproved nature will find satisfaction in a visit to this place, some years ago the haunt of those vagrants known as gypsies." In Dulwich, equally distant from London and in Surrey, "there is a spring of medicinal waters" but it is "most famous for its College" (*The Ambulator*).

[28] A good word for Mark Akenside is unusual. Benjamin Rush called him "cold and formal in his behavior to the Students" (Rush, *Autobiography*, ed. Corner, 53). Another contemporary, Dr. John Coakley Lettsom, ridicules Akenside's appearance and pompous mannerisms and deplores his ruthless ways with pupils and patients (Lettsom's *Ms. Autobiography,* quoted by J. Johnston Abraham, *Lettsom, his life, times, friends and descendants*, 39-42, London, Heinemann, 1933.

[29] Presumably this represented a tailor's bill. WS later refers p. 27 to attending "Mrs. Allison, my Taylor's Wife" on Sunday, October 21 when he "lay'd her of a fine girl."

[30] The lecturer was Dr. Colin Mackenzie of St. Saviour's Churchyard, Southwark, who had been assistant to William Smellie, the celebrated man-midwife, who left London in 1759 (Peachey, 61, 62, 176).

[31] First mention in the diary of an autopsy.

[32] Newington, or Newington Butts, within easy walking distance of St. Thomas's. This village in Surrey was used in Tudor reigns as a practice ground by the archers who went there to shoot at butts as training for their army service (*The Ambulator*).

[33] Skittle grounds or alleys were found around many taverns, *cf*. term *beer and skittles*. The game was similar to Dutch pins or nine pins. In 1780 skittle grounds were abolished by the magistrates, presumably because of dubious conditions surrounding the game at taverns (John Timbs, *Curiosities of London*, 14, London, 1855).

[34] WS often speaks of attending a labour in Crucifix Lane. Probably Colin Mackenzie maintained there a small lying-in hospital for a few poor patients such as WS established near the water front in Letitia Court, Philadelphia, when he began lectures on midwifery in 1765 (Advertisement of Shippen's Midwifery Course, *Penna. Gazette*, January 31, 1765).

August

[1] Dennys De Berdt had a country house in Enfield, Middlesex, ten miles from London, a region well known from Enfield Chace once stocked with deer and other game. In the town there was a meeting house for dissenters (*The Ambulator; Life of Esther De Berdt*, 23).

[2] Miss Tuller, Mr. Gibson and lady are known only as friends of the De Berdts. The location of Mr. Britton's Gardens, or walks, rather (*Latin, potius*), has not been determined.

[3] Mrs. Martha De Berdt, who became her husband's residuary legatee upon his death in 1770 (DNB).

[4] Lewis Way, surgeon to Guy's Hospital 1737-1773 (Wilks and Bettany, 130).

[5] All five of these drugs were standard in the pharmacopeia of the times. *Bezoarticum Jovialis*: a preparation in powder form containing the oxides and probably also various salts of tin, antimony, and mercury. "It is a stupendous Diaphoretick, and prevails against all diseases of the Womb, and many other Diseases of Woman-kind; it prevails also against Fevers, Plague, Scurvy, &c." *Pilulae Rufi*: Rufus's pills, a laxative-cathartic compound of aloes and myrrh, ascribed to Rufus of Ephesus (*ca.* 112 B.C.) and used as late as the twentieth century. *Sal Martis*: sulphate of iron. "The salt of steel is one of the most efficacious preparations of the metal; and not infrequently made use of, in cachectic

and chlorotic cases, for exciting the uterine purgations, strengthening the tone of the viscera, and destroying worms." *Decoctio Valeriani*: a decoction of the roots of Valeriana officinalis; a bitter tonic. *Pulvis Myrrha Compositus*: a powder composed of rue and dittany leaves, myrrh, asafetida, sagapenum, castor, and opopanax. "This is a reformation of the *trochisci e myrrha*, a composition contrived by Razi against uterine obstructions." (Quotations from *Pharmacopoeia Bateana*, or Bate's *Dispensatory*, ed. William Salmon, London, 1700.)

⁶ Mr. Teaber, attendant at Whitefield's Tabernacle, Moorfields, is known to us for no other reason. The three preachers heard on this particular Sunday may have been (1) James Stevens who published *An Elegiac Poem in Memory of George Whitefield*, London, 1770 (BB). (2) The Reverend William Porter, a dissenting minister who married Miss Lowther of Clements Lane in the autumn (*The London Chronicle, October 18-20, 1759*). Did he resemble the Reverend Charles Cummings, a prominent pioneer minister in America? (E. H. Gillett, *History of the Presbyterian Church in the U. S. A.*, 1: 425; 2: 201, Phila., 1864.) (3) The Reverend Howel Davies, a popular preacher of great power who often went on preaching missions with Whitefield and was one of the regular supplies at the Tabernacle and at Tottenham Court Chapel (Tyerman, 2: 48 *n.*).

⁷ The Enfield Assembly was apparently a countrified affair to the eyes of this young man from Philadelphia. The belles he admired come to life only in these pages of the diary.

⁸ The Reverend James Mason, 1705-1763, a dissenting minister whose *Treatise on Self Knowledge*, appearing first in 1745, went through twenty editions (well spaced)" to the honour of public discernment." Mason had a church in Cheshunt, Herts., and also trained pupils for the ministry. He wrote several other books, including *Lord's-Day Evening Entertainments or 52 Sermons on the most serious and important subjects in Divinity to promote Religion in the Family*, 4v. (David Bogue and James Bennett, *A history of dissenters*, 2: 588-590, London, 1833.)

⁹ Shooters Hill, elevation 446 feet, in Woolwich, figures also in the first chapter of *The Tale of Two Cities* by Charles Dickens. Its location on the Dover Road gave it the reputation of being the haunt of highwaymen. The view Shippen describes has been changed beyond recognition by the growth of population and spread of industry.

¹⁰ This Pindaric steed has vanished in the mists of time.

¹¹ Battle of Minden, August 1, 1759.

¹² A false report; General Wedel had been defeated at Zullichau.

¹³ Philadelphia had been gaily illuminated in September 1758, for instance, and "curious Fireworks" displayed on the River Delaware " as a Rejoicing for the Reduction of the Island of Cape Breton and its Dependencies to the obedience of his Brittanick Majesty " (*Penna. Gazette*, September 7, 1758).

¹⁴ Probably the peace-loving Quakers kept their windows dark and the mob resented it.

¹⁵ The coffee house was the place to find a variety of newspapers and to dispatch and receive letters.

¹⁶ Lewis *Dispensatory* refers to a translation of the *Pharmacopeia of the Royal College of Physicians, Edinburgh* by William Lewis, London, 1748, from the fourth edition of the Latin original. Other editions such as Peter Shaw's, 1753, called the book *Pharmacopeia or Dispensatory*.

¹⁷ Evidently Mr. Paul performed an emergency operation.

¹⁸ William Lewis, *A Course of Practical Chemistry. . . . From Lemery, Hoffman, The French Memoirs, The Philosophical Transactions and from the author's own experience*, London, 1746. Lewis was also author of *An Experimental History of the Materia Medica*, which soon after its appearance was presented to the library of the Pennsylvania Hospital by Dr. John Fothergill in 1762 (Montgomery, 346).

[19] Thomas Johnson, an Irish equestrian, made his English debut in 1758, in a field adjoining The Three Hats, a picturesque old inn of the Upper Street, Islington. He would gallop around the field first standing on one horse, then on a pair, then used three horses in turn, and sometimes for a stunt rode a single horse while standing on his head! For ten years he drew crowds and made The Three Hats a popular resort (Warwick Wroth, 142, 148).

[20] Greenwich, a pleasant town in Kent, situated six miles from London (*The Ambulator*).

[21] Eltham, a handsome village eight miles from London and about a mile south of the Dover Road (*ibid.*).

[22] Not only in the pages of Jane Austen and Anthony Trollope were ladies estimated according to their fortunes. *The London Chronicle*, October 25-27, 1759, carried the following announcements:

" Last week Dr. Dolman, physician at Ripon, was married to Miss Reynolds of Moreshaigh in Nottinghamshire, a lady of £10,000 fortune.

" Yesterday was married at St. Olave's Hart-Street, Crutched Friars, Mr. King, Coal Merchant in Mark Lane, to Miss Sunderland of Newcastle, a fortune of £15,000."

[23] The manor of Eltham had been granted to Sir John Shaw by Charles II because of his services to the royal cause. " The estate is now held by his great-great grandson whose elegant seat and plantations do honour to the taste of that gentleman " (*The Ambulator*).

[24] Susanna Shippen born in Philadelphia, 1743; married the Reverend Samuel Blair (the younger), 1769; mother of five children; died in Germantown, 1821 (Nancy Shippen, *Her journal book*, containing *Chart of the descendants of Dr. William Shippen*, compiled by Charles E. Hildeburn).

[25] Mr. Burkitt was Dennys De Berdt's partner in the firm of North America Merchants, Artillery Court, Chiswell Street (*The Universal Director*).

[26] Hertford, twenty-two miles from London, situated at the central part of the Lea valley, with the main river passing through the town near a junction of smaller streams amidst a richly wooded and picturesque country. A place of importance even in Saxon times, it has an old castle (Harold Clunn, *The face of the home counties*, 115, London, Simpkin Marshall, 1937).

[27] Probably the name is Brassey, often seen in books about Hertfordshire. Making a grotto was a favorite hobby of the period, much as making a rock garden has been in our day. Samuel Johnson admired Pope's grotto at Twickenham and described it as " a place of silence and retreat " from which " cares and passions could be excluded " (Johnson, *Lives of the English poets*, 4: 70, London, 1781).

[28] Robert Poole, *A physical vade mecum . . . wherein is contained the Dispensatory of St. Thomas's Hospital with a catalogue of the diseases and the method of their cure prescribed in the said hospital to which is added the Dispensatory of St. Bartholomew's and Guy's Hospital*, London, 1741.

[29] These fifteen young people were attending the fair which was regularly held late in August in Camberwell. Peckham was a sub-division of Camberwell (*Encyclopedia of London*, 73).

[30] Dr. Peter Shaw, FRS, 1694-1763, favorite of King George II, a physician of considerable reputation and a voluminous writer, became licentiate of the Royal College of Physicians 1740, and by royal mandate received an honorary medical degree in 1752 from Cambridge. He was particularly interested in the chemical aspects of medicine (DNB; Munk's *Roll*, 2: 190, 191).

[31] Way and Paul appear in this reference as two conservative surgeons. The extraction operation for cataract, invented as early as 1745 by the French surgeon

Daviel, was coming into favor in England and had actually been improved upon at Guy's Hospital by Samuel Sharp who had invented a beak-shaped knife " to make the incision from within outwards after puncture and counter puncture." His article describing this operation had appeared in 1753 in the *Philosophical Transactions* under title of *New method of opening the cornea in order to extract the crystalline humour*. The old way of dealing with cataract by couching or depression consisted in dislodging the lens with a needle inserted through the cornea and pushing it downward into the lower part of the eyeball where it was expected ultimately to be absorbed or at least to remain permanently out of the line of vision (R. Ruston James, *Studies in the history of ophthalmology in England prior to the year 1800*, 97, 98, Cambridge, The Univ. Press, 1933).

[32] Godding for Godwin? Edward Godwin, one of Whitefield's lay preachers and a writer of hymns and other publications, was popular in London and elsewhere but died in early life. His brother's son, William, married Mary Woolstonecroft whose daughter, Mary, married the poet Shelley (*Life of the Countess of Huntingdon*, 2: 371 *n*.).

[33] Dr. John Fothergill, 1712-1780, Quaker, M. D. from Edinburgh, had an extensive London practice and made valuable contributions to clinical knowledge of the time. His chief interest was botany, particularly the collection and cultivation of exotic plants. His extensive botanical garden at Upton rivaled Kew in its rarities. Realizing the value of exchanging plants of different countries, he maintained an extensive foreign correspondence especially with Americans. Benjamin Franklin was his intimate friend, but every unknown student from the colonies found a welcome in his home (DNB).

[34] Benjamin Cowell, surgeon to St. Thomas's Hospital 1749-1768 (Parsons, 2: 265).

[35] *Touching*, perhaps a technical term in eighteenth-century obstetrics, or else students' jargon, meaning to examine by touch or feeling, or as we say now by palpation, for diagnosis of the stage of labor, position of the foetus, etc.

[36] Glover Hunt, a merchant in Philadelphia. *The Pennsylvania Gazette*, March 4, 1762, carries notice of a sheriff's sale at his house in Market Street where " European and India goods " etc. will be disposed of.

[37] The White Conduit House in the parish of St. James, Clerkenwell, about a mile north of Smithfield, took its name from a water conduit faced with white stone which stood almost opposite. Originally a small seventeenth-century alehouse, it was altered about 1745 and a Long Room added. Tea, coffee, and liquors were sold but its specialties were fresh milk and White Conduit loaves. Cricket could be played in the meadow, bats and balls being furnished by the proprietor (Warwick Wroth, 131-139).

September

[1] Woodford, a village in Essex derives its name from a ford in Epping Forest. About nine miles from London it is remarkable for its fine situation and many handsome homes (*The Ambulator*).

[2] Mrs. Mitchell may have been a prominent dissenter in whose conversation the Countess of Huntingdon took great delight. This Mrs. Mary Mitchell, daughter of Bishop Burnett, was " a woman of great piety and benevolence " who died at her home in Bloomsbury in 1783 and was buried in St. James Church, Clerkenwell, near her father. Perhaps she had a country home in Woodford (*Life of the Countess of Huntingdon*, 40, 40 *n*.).

[3] Wanstead, six miles from London, a village in Essex, adjoining Woodford. " In this place and its neighborhood are several fine seats of the nobility, gentry and wealthy citizens but their lustre is eclipsed by Wanstead House," Lord Tynley's mansion (*The Ambulator*). Wanstead House was pulled down in 1822 but the

two hundred acre park surrounding it was purchased for the public in 1880 (Muirhead's *London Guide*, London, Ernest Benn, 1949).

[4] A chariot was a small private coach.

[5] Chigwell, an ancient village two miles northeast of Woodford, being adjacent to both Epping and Hainault Forests, was much frequented for woodland scenery and pleasing views. A mineral spring discovered in the seventeenth century once brought many visitors. The Grammar School is supposed to have been attended by William Penn, 1644-1718, the founder of Pennsylvania (Harold Clunn, *The face of the home counties*, 116, London, Simpkin Marshall, 1936).

[6] Bartholomew Fair, observed at this period on September 3 to commemorate St. Bartholomew's Day, was held in West Smithfield near the Priory Church. Originally in the twelfth century a fair conducted by the friars, it became secularized and cheapened until its festivities lasting two weeks became a nuisance. It was suppressed in 1855 (E. Beresford Chancellor, *The pleasure haunts of London*, 320-325, Boston, Houghton Mifflin, 1925).

[7] Joseph Warner, 1717-1801, became apprentice to Guy's Hospital, 1734; appointed surgeon to Guy's, 1745, he served until 1790 (Wilks and Bettany, 129). His method of urethral repair seems unusual.

In one form of the operation for hare-lip the edges of the wound were not stitched together with thread as customarily. Instead fine steel pins were thrust through the lip, in on one side of the line of juncture and out on the other, and thread was wound in a figure-of-eight around the projecting ends of each pin to hold it in place. This method suggests one employed sometimes in cookery to close the incision made for stuffing a large fowl or turkey. A set of hare-lip pins is on display among medical curiosities in the library of the University of Rochester Medical School, Rochester, New York.

[8] *Trollopes* were long loose dresses much in favor at this period of the eighteenth century (OED).

[9] Camberwell, a large and pleasant village in Surrey two miles from Southwark in the Dover Road (*The Ambulator*).

[10] Shippen's ballroom standards had been formed in his native city where society leaders had organized in 1748 their exclusive Philadelphia Assemblies. These well-managed functions, the oldest series of subscription balls in the United States, are still in existence today. William Shippen is listed as one of the directors from 1780-1800. In 1795 Moreau de St. Méry complained to John Vaughan, his colleague in the Philosophical Society, that his application for a ticket to the Washington's Birthday Ball, given by the Philadelphia Assembly managers, had been turned down because of St. Méry's occupation in trade as bookseller (Joseph Patterson Sims, *The Philadelphia Assemblies*, Phila., privately printed, 1947; Kenneth and Anna M. Roberts, *Moreau de St. Méry's American Journey*, 333, N. Y., Doubleday, 1947).

[11] The sudden mention, in the diary, of cases of smallpox in London, and in his visits to Enfield does not mean that an unusual epidemic was in progress. The London bills of mortality, conveniently abstracted in *The history of epidemics in Great Britain*, by Charles Creighton, Cambridge, 1894, show that the average annual mortality from smallpox in London in the eight years 1753-1760 was about 2,000; in 1759 it was 2,596. Since the mortality from smallpox varies from 2 to 50 per cent of all cases, according to the severity prevailing at a given time and place, there must have been in the eighteenth century scores of cases of the diseases in London all the time and at times many hundreds. About one in ten of the deaths from all causes was caused by smallpox. At the time of writing this footnote (March 1949) there were no cases in Great Britain and only two in the entire United States (*U. S. Public Health Reports*).

[12] WS was reading with enthusiasm at 7 A. M. Joseph Warner, *Cases in Surgery with remarks; to which is added an account of the preparation and effects of the Agaric of Oak in Stopping of Bleedings after some of the most capital operations,* London, 1754. The book was popular enough to go into a second edition the same year. The cases are "related with brevity, skill and judgment" and range over the entire field of surgery (Wilks and Bettany, 129-130).

[13] Mr. Lawson, now unknown, resembled Francis Alison, D. D., 1705-1779, Vice-Provost of the College of Philadelphia and assistant pastor of the First Presbyterian Church, Philadelphia (W. B. Sprague, *Annals of the American Pulpit,* 3: 73-76, Phila., 1857-1869).

[14] Lively little Mr. Edwards was perhaps the Reverend David Edwards who published in 1770 a small book: *A Minister Dead Yet Speaketh, the substance of two discourses occasioned by the death of the Rev. George Whitefield* (BB; Tyerman 2: 621, 623). Mr. Thomas Adams was an active Methodist lay-preacher, beloved by Whitefield who left him £50 in his will. He had become founder and pastor of a tabernacle in Rodborough, Gloucestershire (*ibid.,* 2: 224, 448, 609).

[15] Ralph Ashton or Assheton, 1736-1773, and George Glentworth, 1735-1792, two young Philadelphians both of whom studied medicine in Edinburgh, got their medical degrees at St. Andrews upon recommendation of Dr. John Hope, 1725-1786, Professor of Botany and Materia Medica, University of Edinburgh, and others. In all probability Glentworth and Ashton did not meet the requirement for length of residence at the University of Edinburgh necessary for a medical degree but could secure degrees at St. Andrews by presenting Edinburgh credentials and by payment of fees. J. B. Salmond, Keeper of the Muniments, St. Salvator's Hall, University of St. Andrews has kindly supplied a copy of *Senate Minute,* March 17, 1759, reporting the conferring of the Degree of Doctor of Medicine on George Glentworth and another *Senate Minute* of August 1, 1759, conferring the medical degree upon Ralph Ashton. In personal communication Dr. Douglas Guthrie, Lecturer on the History of Medicine at the University of Edinburgh, has explained the relationships between Edinburgh and Aberdeen at this period.

[16] Weed Yard does not appear in any map of Southwark nor is it listed in Stow's *Survey of London,* 1755.

[17] John Hunter's anatomical curiosities were as yet in their infancy. Both John and William Hunter spent years in assembling important collections of anatomical and pathological specimens. John Hunter's collections were purchased after his death by the Government for £15,000 and presented to the Royal College of Surgeons in London where they were housed in six large rooms and classified as normal or abnormal forms. William Hunter's collections were bequeathed to the University of Glasgow (which had honored him with an M. D. degree in 1750) and form that institution's medically famous Hunterian Museum (DNB; John H. Teacher, *Catalogue of the Anatomical and Pathological Preparations of Dr. William Hunter,* 2v., Glasgow, 1900). Most unfortunately John Hunter's collections in London were largely destroyed by the blitz in World War II.

[18] Sadler's Hall Feast and Ball took WS to the old Saddlery district in Cheapside. The Saddler's Guild which from early times had supplied horsemen with their accoutrements is traditionally the oldest of the livery companies which were formed to protect and advance the interests of tradesmen. Each guild had its hall for business meetings and occasional festivals where sumptuous dinners and entertainments were offered (*Encyclopedia of London,* 256-257).

[19] Dr. Ralph Assheton's life was a short one. He died in 1773, aged thirty-seven, leaving a wife and several small children (Edward L. Clark, *Record of the inscriptions of Christ Church,* Phila., 1864). George Glentworth, who was his medical classmate in Scotland, became well known in Philadelphia, through activi-

ties as a surgeon in the Revolution, in the formation of the College of Physicians, and in the opening of a small inoculation hospital in 1773 during a smallpox epidemic. He is said to have died of yellow fever in the terrible outbreak of 1793 in Philadelphia (Packard, **1**: 89, 136).

[20] Probably Henry Reed, an elderly minister, previously (p. 11) mentioned. Mr. Condor was John Conder, D. D., 1714-1781, of Little Moorfields Chapel (DNB).

[21] Tourmaline, a pyro-electric mineral, has important modern use in the tourmaline tongs of the jeweler, in optical work and for measuring the intensity of radium emanations (OED).

[22] Captain Blair may have been either John or Francis Blair whose ships ran in and out of Philadelphia at this period.

[23] " The busy and uproarious throng of Southwark Fair yearly in September filled the High Street and its purlieus from St. Margaret's Hill to St. George's church" (William Rendle, *Old Southwark and its people*, 33, London, 1878). This fair of ancient origin, described by both Evelyn and Pepys, was suppressed as a nuisance in 1763 (John Timbs, *Curiosities of London*, 675, London, 1855).

[24] Hervey's D. may well have been the *Dialogues of Theron and Aspasio*, a defence of evangelical principles written by James Hervey, the rector of Weston-Flavell and Collingtree, "a very popular divine of exemplary piety and virtue" (BB). Hervey treasured his friendship with Whitefield and the Countess of Huntingdon but had become alienated from Wesley because of doctrinal differences. In the first nine months after its appearance in 1754 *Theron and Aspasio* was bought by 10,000 eager readers of its first and second editions and a third edition was demanded (Luke Tyerman, *Oxford Methodists*, 256, 304, London, 1872; *Life of the Countess of Huntingdon*, **1**: 187-189). With more critical acumen Lecky describes Hervey as a "master of tumid and over-ornamented rhetoric so attractive to half-educated minds" (Lecky, **3**: 39).

[25] Dr. John Guyse, 1680-1761, "an eminent, independent dissenting Divine" (BB) was an active member of the King's Head Society which rendered assistance to young men in securing academic training for the ministry. He had helped raise funds for the College of New Jersey (Wertenbaker, 33; DNB).

[26] Mr. Alexander was perhaps a visitor from America. A Mr. Alexander Alexander, tutor in the College of Philadelphia in 1764, graduated there 1765. He may have had a previous period of foreign study (Montgomery, 425).

[27] Seeing Garrick as Archer is the first mention WS makes of theatre-going.

[28] This smallpox patient was Esther De Berdt, born in 1747. In a portrait show-ing a family group she appeared as a girl "slight in frame with light hair, fair complexion and an air of intelligence and refinement." As she grew up "her reading of a serious cast included Hervey, Watts, Shenstone and Young. The theatre then more attractive than ever, Garrick being in the flush of his wonderful celebrity, and the dramatic talent of the day at work to give scope to his varied genius, seems to have been prohibited by the discipline of Artillery Court" (*Life of Esther De Berdt*, 23). Esther explained her frequent ill turns of health by saying "God has been pleased to afflict me with a feeble, disordered body."

[29] *Biographia Brittanica* lists a Reverend James Howell, M. A., author of a sermon published 1780 who might have been this preacher. If Shippen intended to write "Howell Harris" he would have meant a preacher of some temporary im-portance who often served as Whitefield's understudy, the man who later helped to reconcile the differences between Whitefield and Wesley (Tyerman, **1**: 281, 531, 541).

[30] Miss Britton was undoubtedly the daughter of Mr. Britton whose gardens, "walks, potius," WS had admired in Enfield on August 3.

October

[1] Mr. Hunter's house was in the Great Piazza, Covent Garden (see page 71).

[2] Dr. Hunter began his " autumn course " of anatomical lectures regularly in October. This course ran until New Year's Day or a little later. He began his " spring course " about January 20 and continued lecturing until late in the spring (Peachey, 90, 91).

[3] Robin Hood was a tavern famous for debates of the Robin Hoodians who held their meetings at this place every Monday night. Forty-six citizens were admitted to the gathering without restriction on payment of sixpence. A varied assortment of politicians, literary men, artists, actors, wits, and freethinkers made its sessions lively. Burke and lesser speakers used the tavern as a place to practice their oratory. Horace Walpole wrote (November 9, 1764) that a visit to this club must not be missed by a London sightseer (Austin Dobson 3: 76; Fielding's *Covent Garden Journal*, ed. Jensen, 1(9): 128, 129).

[4] See page 75.

[5] See page 75.

[6] A box might cost five shillings, a seat in the pit could be had for three, half a crown brought a good place in the gallery, a shilling admitted to the upper gallery; and late arrivals after the first play was over got reduced rates of admission (newspaper advertisements of the period).

[7] See page 76.

[8] *The Gentleman's Magazine*, Historical Chronicle, September, 1759, briefly notes the death on September 4 of Dr. Middleton of Cateaton Street; the *London Chronicle*, September 1-4, 1759 expands the report: " Yesterday died at his house in Cateaton Street near Guildhall, of a violent fever, Dr. Middleton, an eminent man-midwife." In spite of his eminence and possession of a medical library good enough to attract John Hunter to its sale, Dr. Middleton nevertheless receives no mention in any history of midwifery or obstetrics now readily obtainable.

[9] Thomas Sydenham, 1624-1689, whose great medical treatise in Latin appeared in innumerable editions, was a venerated authority for the internist for more than a hundred years. His *Opera Universa* (London, 1685) was translated into English in 1696 and had received a recent edition in 1753 to which Shippen undoubtedly had access. To this edition there had been added *explanatory notes teaching the practice of inoculation, the use of chalybeates and mineral waters, with the remedies and regimen proper for nephritic patients*. The introduction of such notes would perhaps have irritated the original author by their emphasis upon system and their new-fangled practices.

[10] See page 76.

[11] C. Blair probably means Captain Blair previously mentioned.

[12] Quebec fell to the English September 13, 1759.

[13] By the terms of William Harvey's bequest the Harveiian oration must follow certain stereotyped lines. Once a year a general feast for all fellows of the Royal College of Physicians was to be declared and " on the day when such feast shall be kept, some one person of the said College shall be from time to time appointed by the President and the two eldest Censors and two eldest Elects for the time being of the said College" (to avoid successive appointments of the same man) " who shall make an oration in Latin publicly." The oration was to be " a commemoration of all the benefactors of the College by name . . . an exhortation to imitate these benefactors . . . an exhortation to fellows and members of the said College to search and study out the secrets of nature by way of experiment." Orators were to be paid five pounds and many of the orations, including Mark Akenside's, were printed (Munk's *Roll*, 3: 360, 361).

[14] J. Mathers may have been a Philadelphian. The play given that night at Drury Lane was *Richard III* with Garrick in the title role. At Covent Garden *The Beggar's Opera* was having a six weeks run which started October 10 (Genest IV, Entries for October, 1759).

[15] Percival Pott, 1713-1788, a distinguished surgeon at St. Bartholomew's Hospital, was the author of *Observations on that disorder of the corner of the eye commonly called Fistula lachrymalis*, which appeared in 1758. He wrote voluminously on many subjects of surgical interest (see page 57).

[16] John Douglas, 1727-1758, was an early private teacher of anatomy. His lectures, advertised in the *London Evening Post*, September 21, 1752, continued until his untimely death at thirty-one in 1758. His *Treatise on Hydrocele* appeared in 1755. He has been often confused with John Douglas, surgeon, who died in 1743 (Peachey, 22-24).

[10] See page 76.

[18] Mr. Drinker was, of course, one of the well-known Philadelphia family of that name; perhaps Henry Drinker of the firm of James and Drinker, importers, which carried on an extensive trade in its own ships prior to the Revolution (Cecil K. Drinker, *Not so long ago*, 5, N. Y., Oxford Univ. Press, 1937).

November

[1] St. George's Hospital dates from its establishment at Hyde Park Corner in Lanesborough House, 1733, then a country location. John Hunter, 1728-1793, was a member of its surgical staff from 1768 until the day of his death (see p. 73). Caesar Hawkins, 1711-1786, acquired a large practice as the result of his surgical skill demonstrated at St. George's 1734-1774. William Bromfield, 1712-1792, served as surgeon at St. George's 1744-1780. He had also given private instruction in " anatomy, chirurgical operations and bandages " from 1735-1750. In 1747 he received appointment as surgeon to H. R. H., The Prince of Wales, later George III (J. Blomfield, *St. George's 1733-1933*, 111, 112, London, The Medici Society, 1933 Anniversary Volume).

[2] See page 76.

[3] A demonstration made by vivisection (see p. 69).

[4] St. Bartholomew's Hospital was founded in 1123 by Rahere, a courtier who vowed when prostrated by severe illness in Rome that he would establish a place for care of the sick if he recovered. Among many well known physicians in past attendance at St. Bartholomew's, William Harvey is outstanding in the seventeenth century for lectures on the circulation of the blood (*Encyclopedia of London*, 389, 391).

[5] See page 57.

[6] Messrs. Sansom and Swett carried a varied stock of merchandise at their store in Front Street, Philadelphia. In the winter of 1762 issues of the *Pennsylvania Gazette* carried notice of their removal to a new location " in Water Street between Market and Arch nearly opposite the old Ferry-house " where they continued to display many foreign wares and liquors.

[7] Sir Thomas Chitty, Knight, Alderman of the Tower Ward, had been elected Lord Mayor of London on Michaelmas Day, 1759, for a year's term. On November 9, the Lord Mayor Elect, accompanied by a procession, in which two gigantic carved wooden figures, Gog and Magog, had a place of honor, proceeded in state to the Royal Courts of Justice to make declaration of his fealty before His Majesty's judges. In the evening at the Guildhall the new Mayor and his sheriffs entertained at an elaborate banquet, and there were lesser banquets and balls throughout the city (*London Chronicle*, September 29-October 2, 1759; *Encyclopedia of London*, 211, 212).

[8] Mr. Wyckoff's identity is a puzzle. A Peter Wyckoff, 1735-1804, who became a merchant in Philadelphia may have been Shippen's friend. Early Philadelphia directories (1791 and 1794) list Wyckoff and Harrison, Druggists, 41 High Street (M. B. Streeter and Mrs. M. B. Streeter, *The Wyckoff family in America*, 446, Rutland, Vt., Tuttle Co., 1934).

[9] Gerardus Clarkson, 1737-1790, was a former schoolmate of Shippen at West Nottingham Academy. He studied medicine in Philadelphia as the apprentice of Dr. Thomas Bond, and at this time was making a grand tour of medical centers in Great Britain, and on the continent (Rush, *Autobiography*, ed. Corner, 189, 190; Hall and Clarkson, *Memoirs of Matthew Clarkson and his brother, Gerardus Clarkson*, 96, 97, Phila., Thomson Printing Co., 1890).

[10] See page 76.

[11] The play at Drury Lane that evening was Ben Jonson's *Every Man in His Own Humour* (Genest, 4: 578).

[12] Captain Budden of the *Philadelphia Packet* had apparently brought WS some apples from America.

[13] See page 76.

[14] See page 77 n.

[15] *The Pennsylvania Gazette* lists Seth Ewer as a sea captain who once commanded the Sloop *Sea-flower*. Joseph Shippen's letter book (HSP) mentions dining with a Mr. Ewer who was probably a London merchant.

[16] *The London Gazette*, October 23-27, had printed his Majesty's Proclamation for Public Thanksgiving on Thursday, November 27. A similar proclamation was issued for Scotland. Sermons were preached in all the churches and prayers of gratitude were offered for a harvest of victories. George Whitefield had begun preaching Thanksgiving sermons in October (Tyerman, 2: 422; see page 82).

December

[1] First night performance of Oronooko at Drury Lane (Genest, 4: 578).

[2] See page 68.

[3] See page 76.

[4] Susanna Cibber, 1714-1766, sister of the musician Thomas Arne, was known not only for distinguished powers as a tragic actress but for her lovely voice heard to advantage in Händel's Messiah in contralto airs specially written for her (*The Age of Johnson, Essays Presented to Chauncey Brewster Tinker*, 413-417, New Haven, Yale Univ. Press, 1949).

[5] The cranberries for the "pye" must have been sent from Philadelphia. It was apparently the custom to send food packages to England in spite of the danger of spoilage on the long voyage. Esther De Berdt Reed, writing in 1772 to her mother in England promises "to send some cranberries and some sturgeon and if possible some venison hams, but they are now so scarce it is difficult to procure any" (*Life of Esther De Berdt*, 171).

[6] See page 77.

[7] See page 77.

[8] Thomas Penn, *ca.* 1701-1775, son of William Penn, the Founder, and his second wife Hannah Callowhill, had married in 1751 Lady Juliana Fermor, b. 1729, the youngest daughter of the Earl of Pomfret, by whom he had eight children, four of whom did not survive the rigors of an eighteenth-century childhood. At the time of their wedding Peter Van Dyck's portrait of Lady Juliana showed her as "a well-looking lady in her wedding dress of white silk" while her husband was depicted as "a perfectly dressed and somewhat precise gentleman," a very elegant bridegroom, "in his embroidered grayish blue coat and breeches and long white

satin waistcoat." (Howard M. Jenkins, *The family of William Penn, Founder of Pennsylvania, ancestry and descendants*, 129-152, Phila., 1899). Miss Frame was undoubtedly Philadelphia Hannah Freame, niece of Thomas Penn and Lady Juliana. The daughter of Thomas Freame and his wife Margaret Penn, this girl was born in Philadelphia in 1740 while her parents were trying to adjust themselves to conditions in the colonies. Philadelphia Hannah married an Irish gentleman in 1770 and became Lady Cremorne. Her portrait by Sir Joshua Reynolds was hung in the Penn mansion at Stoke Pogis (*ibid.*, 89, 90).

[9] Philadelphia papers mention Captain McClelland as in charge of various ships at this period.

[10] See page 77.

[11] *The Refusal* was presented at Drury Lane (Genest, 4: 579) on December 19, 21, and 27.

[12] Sunday, December 23, 1759, " about four in the morning a fire broke out at a Cabinet-maker's in King Street, Covent Garden, which entirely consumed that house and two more in front; a large workshop backwards took fire, and having no water for some time, the flames soon reached several houses in Hart Street. . . . It is computed that about fifty houses are consumed and several more greatly damaged. One fireman and a brewer's servant lost their lives by the fall of a house, and several others had their arms and legs broke. . . . Loss is computed at more than £70,000 " (*Gentleman's Magazine*, December, 1759).

[13] Among entries from the Historical Chronicle of *The Gentleman's Magazine*, December 1759 the following are quoted:

" *Royal Family at St. James*. Tuesday, December 25. Being Christmas Day and a high festival at Court, his Majesty preceded by heralds, pursuivants &c, went to the Chapel Royal at St. James's and heard a sermon preached by Rev. Dr. Newton and afterwards came into the chapel and received the sacrament with the Royal Family and offered a purse of gold for the poor.

" *Money for Fire Sufferers*, Thursday, December 27. Dr. Ward sent this day a benefaction of £50 to the subscription offered at Slaughter's Coffee House for the relief of the distress'd sufferers by the late fire in Covent Garden." [Dr. Joshua Ward, 1685-1761, was a quack doctor whose cure-alls were immensely popular (DNB).]

[14] Chelsea College, or Hospital, founded about 1618, housed old and disabled soldiers in beautiful quarters designed by Sir Christopher Wren. The place was run like a garrison with a program of duties including turns for all, and the pensioners wore uniforms with red coats lined in blue and three-cornered cocked hats. By " the Queen's bounty " they were given a small allowance of tobacco daily. The institution's collection of military portraits, battle flags and trophies made it a show place. It was situated close to Ranelagh whose gardens are now incorporated in the hospital grounds (John Timbs, *Curiosities of London*, 77-79, London, 1855). In 1950, in spite of damage by blitz in World War II, this institution is still pursuing its merciful course. Bedridden pensioners are now sent to a hospital at the seaside.

[15] Shippen probably went with his friend to the Cock Tavern in Fleet Street, where a gilded cock designed by Grinling Gibbons marked the door; but there were two other Cock Taverns in London. One in Threadneedle Street, facing the north gate of the Royal Exchange, was known for the excellence of its soups served in silver at an economical price. The other Cock Tavern, kept by Oxford Kate in Bow Street, had the reputation of being a gathering place for shady characters from the underworld (John Timbs, *Club life in London*, 131 ff., London, 1866).

[16] Cousin Sterling was Dorothy Willing Sterling, daughter of William Shippen's Aunt Anne, Mrs. Charles Willing (see p. 81).

[17] Thomas Willing of Bristol and London was Dorothy Willing Sterling's bachelor uncle, her father's younger brother, who was a director of the Bank of England. He died in Longford, Middlesex in 1770 (R. Winder Johnson, *The ancestry of Rosalie Morris Johnson*, 241, Phila., privately printed Ferris and Leach, 1905).

[18] Esther De Berdt, 1747-1785, was a little girl of twelve when WS first knew her. In 1770 at twenty-three she married Joseph Reed of Philadelphia, who had studied law at the Temple, and went to live in Pennsylvania. As the wife of Washington's military secretary she shared her husband's prominence. During the Revolution she raised a large sum of money to aid the soldiers in Washington's army (*Life of Esther De Berdt*, 317). Her early death before she was forty was greatly deplored.

[19] The " famous Mr. Edwards " among the dissenters was John Edwards of Leeds who " had withdrawn from Mr. Wesley and built himself a place of worship called White Chapel where he continued to dispense the word of life for more than thirty years " after a stormy period of persecution which had made him conspicuous (*Life of the Countess of Huntingdon*, 1: 161, 286, 352, 396). The Anglican clergyman, the Reverend Thomas Edwards, 1729-1785, was actually more truly famous for his *New Translation of the Psalms*, 1755, and for a later work of some importance in the Calvinist and Arminian controversy, *The Doctrine of Irresistible Grace proved to have no foundation in the Writings of the New Testament*, 1759 (DNB).

[20] Tench Francis, 1730-1800, son of the Attorney General of Pennsylvania of the same name who died in 1758, was one of Philadelphia's wealthy citizens, said to be agent for the Penns in America, whose abilities as a financier were recognized by his appointment as the first cashier of the Bank of the United States (Henry Simpson, *Lives of eminent Philadelphians now deceased*, 376, Philadelphia, 1859). He was senior partner of the Philadelphia firm, Francis and Relfe, importing merchants (Letters of Joseph Shippen, HSP).

January, 1760

[1] Mr. J. Ewer was probably an English merchant.

[2] The firm of Sargent and Aufrère had many dealings with Philadelphians (Joseph Shippen's Letters, HSP).

[3] Mr. Pitt's speeches referring to Quebec had been given November 14 and November 21, 1759 (Basil Williams, *The Life of William Pitt, First Earl of Chatham*, 2: 13, London, Longmans Green, 1913).

[4] Sophia, daughter and heiress of Georges René Aufrère, Esq. of Chelsea, married before she was twenty C. Anderson Pelham, Esq., Recorder of Great Grimsby (later Baron Yarborough), and was painted by Sir Joshua Reynolds as " Mrs. Pelham Feeding Chickens." A charming mezzotint engraving of this portrait, executed by Dickinson, 1779, hangs in a corridor of the New York Public Library (*A catalogue raisonné of the engraved works of Sir Joshua Reynolds from 1755-1822*, 126, London, 1884).

[5] Kinship between Tench Francis and the Shippens became very close. His sister Margaret had been married in 1753 to Edward Shippen who later became Chief Justice of Pennsylvania. Tench Francis himself married in 1762 Anne Willing, daughter of Charles Willing and Anne Shippen Willing, and thus a cousin of William Shippen's (R. Winder Johnson, *The ancestry of Rosalie Morris Johnson*, 240, Phila., privately printed Ferris and Leach, 1905).

[6] Captain Richard Budden of the *Pennsylvania Packet*; Captain John Bolitho's ship was the *Myrtilla*.

[7] No papers of special importance were given at the Royal Society that evening.

[8] Holding Court functions during holidays.

[9] Henry Fielding's description of the Mob lists its pretensions as " exclusive right to the River Thames, possession of the whole Street (having lately made such a Disposition of their Waggons, Carts and Drays that no Coach can pass along without the utmost Difficulty and Danger), the same pretensions to possession of the Highways, and the Right of Excluding all Women of Fashion out of St. James's Park on Sunday Evening . . . lately asserted with great Vehemence . . . and have inflicted the Punishment of Mobbing on several Ladies who had transgressed without design " (Fielding's *Covent Garden Journal*, ed. Jensen, 2(49): 33-35).

[10] See page 77.

[11] William Franklin, the natural son of Benjamin Franklin, was born about 1731, shortly before BF's marriage to Deborah Read. Young Franklin, approaching thirty, was now studying law at the Temple. In 1763 he became the last royalist governor of New Jersey. During the Revolution his loyalist sympathies led to his arrest and a period of exile in Connecticut. His last years were spent in England where he died in 1813 (DNB).

[12] See page 77 n.

[13] James Fordyce, D. D., 1720-1796, minister to the Presbyterian congregation in Monkwell, was well-liked by Dr. Samuel Johnson " whom he celebrated . . . in a warm strain of devotional composition " (Boswell's *Johnson*, ed. Ingpen, 2: 1136).

Summer at St. Thomas's

ALMOST two hundred years have passed since William Shippen, Jr., wrote his diary in London. Here is a little book which charms by its combination of naïveté with complete seriousness of purpose. The author is no poseur; he does not seek to instruct; he never moralizes. His hastily written entries in every day language are a simple memorandum of what has happened. He introduces us to an eighteenth century in action—doctors in the hospital, preachers in the church, actors on the stage, John and William Hunter in their dissecting rooms. As we turn the pages of the diary we see revealed the private world of a young man who passed his twenty-second birthday at sea on the way to England during a tedious voyage of seven and a half weeks. He has come to London to take advantage of educational opportunities which are lacking in the colonies where there are few hospitals, only an occasional doctor lecturing on anatomy, and no medical schools. In the summer of 1759 he begins reporting the events of his life as he follows the surgical practice of St. Thomas's Hospital in Southwark near London Bridge.[1]

At this location, where all the great southern roads converge upon London, there had been a place for the care of the sick and suffering among the traders, travelers, and pilgrims since the early days of the Priory of St. Mary Overie, and it is thought that St. Thomas's evolved from this start, receiving its name after the canonization of Thomas à Becket. In the sixteenth century, after the secularization of church property under Henry VIII, it became necessary to close the hospital for a few years, greatly to the loss of its possible beneficiaries. When it was reorganized, the fame of Thomas à Becket was in total eclipse and the hospital of St. Thomas the Apostle, as it was henceforth to be called, received in 1553, together with the hospitals of Christ and Bridewell, a

---

[1] See Parsons, **2**, chap. X, as the basis of this account.

50

foundation charter or a grant from Edward VI turning this institution over to " the mayor, commonalty and citizens of the City of London " to be administered by a Court of Governors.[2] In the eighteenth century St. Thomas's had been rebuilt and enlarged to meet the needs of its populous neighborhood. It was arranged in a series of quadrangles. Women patients were in wards at the front of the hospital, next came administrative quarters, behind these offices were men's wards, and lastly, in what was called the " Back Yard," the " Foul Wards," where venereal disease of both sexes received treatment.

Shippen's days as pupil at St. Thomas's soon fell into a pattern. Every Thursday, he notes, was " taking in day " when new patients were admitted to the hospital after examination. This could be an educative process for an observant pupil. On Thursday morning outpatients were also seen by a senior physician. Tuesday was regularly physicians' day when the physicians examined and prescribed for all patients bedded in St. Thomas's. Every Saturday physicians and surgeons together made rounds through all the wards. On Wednesdays male outpatients were seen by a junior physician; on Fridays women and children were examined. Operations seem to have been performed as necessity demanded. Minor surgery might be done on Monday before the week's program speeded up. In 1759, by reciprocal arrangement, surgeons were making rounds at St. Thomas's on Tuesdays, Thursdays, and Saturdays, and at Guy's on Mondays, Wednesdays, and Fridays, so that a surgeon was never lacking in the neighborhood, an important matter in the days before resident house officers. Nursing was done by an inadequate number of women of servant status, untrained practical attendants who merely waited on the sick. Three senior physicians and three senior surgeons divided responsibilities for the patients. Each surgeon had one or more apprentices bound to him at Surgeons Hall for a term of seven years of thorough training. Ranking below apprentices were the surgeon's dressers who in the 1750's carried dressings and instruments but who later in the century performed minor operations and handled accident cases. Pupils appear to have been

[2] Parsons, 1: 119-142.

spectators in the hospital, there to learn by looking. It must be remembered that, although pupils were not organized to assist in working the hospital practice, these young men had already served or were engaged in serving as apprentices to reputable doctors, and each one of them was required to present a certificate of recommendation from his preceptor before admission to hospital privileges. Each surgeon took three or four pupils, as many as he could conscientiously manage. These pupils were charged twenty-four guineas for a twelve-months' course or eighteen guineas for six months' attendance. Nominally attached to one surgeon, each pupil had the privilege of following his master's colleagues and could attend the operations but not the practice at Guy's Hospital across the street; and a pupil at Guy's enjoyed similar favors at St. Thomas's until a feud broke out between the two hospitals and temporarily (until 1768) destroyed the relationship. William Shippen (who dropped the Jr. from his name while in London) has left no record of being attached to any one particular surgeon during his months at St. Thomas's, and it is probable that he was allowed the privilege of being a " pupil at large," free to learn methods where he could. Elementary lectures on anatomy, surgery, medicine, and chemistry were available at this time at one or the other of the hospitals upon payment of extra fees. Shippen did not attend any of these courses as he had already dedicated himself to obstetrics as a specialty and had selected William Hunter's school for instruction in anatomy. During the summer he was kept busy by the stimulating Dr. Mackenzie whose lectures on midwifery, first noted in late July in the diary, kept him increasingly occupied until October when Hunter's school opened.

Dr. Colin Mackenzie,[3] a man of medical consequence esteemed by John and William Hunter and a partner in some of their researches, is entirely forgotten today. He made no contributions to medical literature and what we know about him personally is largely gained from William Wadd's agreeable medical gossip.[4]

[3] Peachey, 176-179.
[4] Two books by William Wadd are devoted to personalities about his medical contemporaries: *Nugae Chirugicae, or a Biographical Miscellany* . . . London,

Mackenzie was a bachelor, formerly surgeon to a man-of-war, who began to teach midwifery in the Borough of Southwark during the winter of 1754-1755. Professionally he had gained favor as assistant to William Smellie, the well known man-midwife who retired to Scotland in 1759. Mackenzie had many friends, gave jolly dinners, kept a good cellar, and amassed a considerable fortune. Although he is said to have contributed to the medical thought of his day, we can evaluate him only through John Hunter's report and by a late eighteenth-century book of William Perfect's entitled *Cases in Midwifery Principally Founded on the Correspondence of the late learned and ingenious Dr. Colin Mackenzie.*[5]

Mackenzie's methods of teaching seem to have been thoroughly modern in character. Under his instruction William Shippen ceased to be an onlooker. He not only attended labours in Crucifix Lane, he delivered patients, scorning delights and living laborious days which might extend to their full twenty-four hours when he was called upon a case. Dr. Mackenzie must have maintained in Crucifix Lane a small private hospital for lying-in care of poor women where he made demonstration of obstetrical principles in connection with his course of midwifery lectures given outside the Borough hospitals as an independent venture.[6] It was here no doubt that William Shippen in the course of his instruction examined seventeen pregnant women one day, as he notes in his diary. Colin Mackenzie's residence at this time was in St. Saviour's Churchyard,[7] known as " a semi-fashionable haunt of noted doctors," a location conveniently near St. Thomas's and Guy's. The *Gentleman's Magazine* of February, 1775, carries a notice of his death in the previous month on January 31. His estate of £10,000 was left to his brother, the Laird of Muirton. Dr. Orme, man-midwife of Threadneedle Street, paid a thousand pounds for his medical museum specimens.[4]

William Shippen's London as he grew to know it that summer

1824; *Mems., Maxims and Memoirs*, London, 1827 (pp. 285-286 relate to Mackenzie).

[5] Third edition, 1790, published at Rochester, England.

[6] Peachey, 177.

[7] William Rendle, *Old Southwark and its people*, 200, London, 1878.

in the hospital was quite different from the London familiar to
Samuel Johnson or to Horace Walpole. From the very nature of
his occupation Shippen looked daily at distressing realities.[8] What
havoc malnutrition, overcrowding, and subsequent immorality
where the occasion was always present, had wrought upon the
underpaid, over-exploited, gin-swigging poor who had the mis-
fortune to live in a century of increasing urbanization without
knowledge of proper sanitation, without child labor laws or other
protective legislation; who had to suffer all the ills of the flesh
without knowledge of a variety of controlling drugs and to
undergo the rigors of surgery, when necessary, without benefit of
anesthesia or antisepsis! All this misery William Shippen saw
against the gaudy background of London with its trappings of
luxury and its pickpockets, prostitutes, and excitable mob, Henry
Fielding's " Fourth estate," [9] who swarmed the parks and the
streets and made their passage a hazard day or night, particularly
during celebrations.

Much of the territory within a circuit of twenty-five miles such
as described by *The Ambulator* in its suggested *Tour Round
London*, grew familiar that summer to William Shippen. Coaches
proceeded at a leisurely pace, to be sure, and only the newest ones
were supplied with springs, but nobody was in a hurry or expected
luxurious comfort in these conveyances. Travel by horseback
along frequented routes could be a pleasant pastime and was
perhaps more dependable for speed. Turnpikes were coming in,
but paying toll on these roads was protested, sometimes by riots.
It would not be until the conclusion of the Seven Years War that
road building and highway maintenance would receive serious
support in the reign of George III. Deep in the country, roads
were often a sea of mud after heavy rains and became impassable
for weeks. It took Thomas Pennant, the naturalist, six weari-
some days in 1739 to go from Chester to London, a distance of
about two hundred miles, and sometimes his coach had to be
dragged out of the slough by six or eight horses.[10] The journey

[8] M. Dorothy George, *London Life in the XVIII century*, N. Y., Knopf, 1925.

[9] Fielding's *Covent Garden Journal*, ed. Jensen, 2(47): 23-26.

[10] Thomas Burke, *Travel in England*, 65, London, Batsford, 1946. Quotation
from Thomas Pennant recalling conditions in 1739.

Fig. 3. St. Thomas's Hospital in 1758.

Fig. 4. Eighteenth - century dancing party.

to Edinburgh, which would become familiar to Shippen before his return to America, varied as to time consumed, taking three weeks sometimes by coach, at other times, if conditions were entirely favorable, only ten days. In 1772 everybody in London was astounded when in forty-three hours of forced riding on horseback a messenger brought news from Edinburgh of an upsetting bankruptcy.[11] The mighty traveler of the English roads in this century was John Wesley, who thought nothing of doing sixty miles a day on horseback, braving rain, frost, snow, or gale to preach the Word to sinners. He often read as he rode, curiously enough, letting the reins hang loose upon the horse's neck and trusting to the Lord to protect against pitfalls.

Shippen was glad to leave " dirty London " whenever he could that summer of 1759 for a visit with his dissenting friends, the De Berdts, who had a country place at Enfield. The De Berdts respected his learning. He advised them on medical matters and even bled them when he thought necessary. Sometimes he went to Peckham with John Latham, a young man of his own age who was a pupil at Guy's. He had plenty of young company at the hospitals, though some of the young men he thought were " boobies." In two or three lines, like an impressionist with quick, vivid strokes, he shows us his landlady serving him an excellent dinner of roast lamb and French beans for sixpence; the coaching party he regaled on a ride from Woodford to London with his story of America; his private patients such as his " barbor's maid " and his "' taylor's wife " whom he " lay'd of a fine girl "; his pretty partners at the balls and assemblies who flit through his pages in figures of the minuet and intricate country dances. He dined with Mr. Franklin of Philadelphia and with Dr. Reeve who had become President of the Royal College of Physicians;[12] he supped with the Reverend George Whitefield; dining, later on, as a guest of an experienced hostess, Mrs. Aufrère, he heard tales of Mr. Pitt's marvelous oratory, and he admired her daughter, " a wonderful girl of seven," whom we know with our superior omniscience will grow up a beauty, to be painted by Sir Joshua Reynolds. Best of all he enjoyed his weekends in the country

[11] Lecky, 7: 223-228.   [12] Munk's *Roll*, 2: 133-134.

where he grew familiar with the charms of the English landscape, its meadows, groves, and ancient castles. He visited Eltham
Palace, Sir John Shaw's estate, and Wanstead House, Lord Tynley's
magnificent mansion. Though the weather was sultry the country
had never looked prettier, Horace Walpole was writing from
Strawberry Hill. "With English verdure" they had "an Italian
summer" of unprecedented heat.[13] Shippen rode to the top of
Shooters Hill one day on horseback and admired the view as he
looked into Essex, Surrey, and part of Sussex, tracing the meander-
ings of the silver-streaming Thames through a widespread lovely
countryside as yet untouched by the progress of industry.

Back from such pleasures the young man would be up at six
next morning at his boarding house not far from the hospital, to
read Warner's *Surgery* or he would hurry off after early breakfast
to St. Thomas's to busy himself professionally with London's sick
poor. In hot city streets Londoners "with eyes full of dust" were
suffering that summer in "a torrent of heat." London had a mid-
summer outbreak of "contagious sore throat" which worried
Horace Walpole. Young Lady Essex died of it in two days.
When two servants at Newcastle House succumbed to it in quick
succession, the Duke fled in terror. The poor could not escape.
Whatever the trouble, many of them must die untended by physicians. Of the babies born more than half would never live
beyond the age of five.[14] No control was exercised over either
milk or water supply. Bacteriology was an undiscovered science.
The art of pediatric care, soundly grounded on scientific knowledge, was to be developed long after the eighteenth-century
slaughter of the innocents by neglect.

At St. Thomas's in 1759-1760 there was a staff of doctors [15]
able enough no doubt for their day. Cheselden was dead, Huck
Saunders and George Fordyce had not yet joined the staff. Shippen
mentions as physicians in attendance at the hospital Thomas Reeve,
Thomas Milner, and Mark Akenside (a minor poet and probably
a minor physician), and as surgeon's Joseph Paul, Benjamin

[13] Walpole, 4: 281, 282, 284.
[14] Caulfield, Ernest, The infant welfare movement in the eighteenth century,
Annals of Med. Hist., n. s. 2: 480-494 (part I); 600-696 (part II), 1930.
[15] Parsons, 2, Lists, 263, 265.

Cowell, and Thomas Baker. At Guy's Hospital, Joseph Warner's abilities as an operator excited Shippen's attention and made him into a faithful student of Warner's textbook which he found illuminating. The eighteenth-century surgeon must be deft and sure. Without the possibility of anesthetic control and with no knowledge of antisepsis, he did not dare invade or explore the great body cavities, but he had plenty of amputations, repair of hernias, removal of external tumors, and cutting for stone to test his skill. For pain-killers he could use opium or whiskey. He must know the fundamentals of anatomy thoroughly and completely, and to this end dissections and operations upon the cadaver were his main study. At St. George's Hospital, Shippen saw a number of operations by two dextrous surgeons, Caesar Hawkins and William Bromfield, both of whom had taught anatomy [16] as a foundation for their specialty years before William Hunter had set up his school with its greater advantages and opportunities. At St. Bartholomew's he was greatly impressed by Percival Pott whose skill was building up for him the largest surgical practice in London. He was a "very clever neat surgeon," Shippen reports. He did the "neatest operation for Bubonocele that I ever saw." Busy as Pott was in hospital and private practice he has left a record of his operative procedures in many publications; his name long clung to a tubercular condition of the spine which he described and to this day surgeons still speak of "Pott's fracture," referring to his description of a particular type of injury to the ankle. Among the doctors with whom Shippen was connected in the London hospitals, Percival Pott is the only one whose reputation survives in twentieth-century practice.

[16] Peachey, 36-37 (Bromfield); 35-36 (Hawkins). Fuller accounts in DNB.

William Shippen and George Whitefield

S UMMER Sundays found young William Shippen among the throngs of the devout who crowded Whitefield's Tabernacle in Moorfields. Whitefield himself was absent from London during most of this summer of 1759 while conducting a preaching mission in Scotland [1] but his pulpit was supplied by a succession of dissenting Calvinistic ministers who kept his followers in line against their leader's return. For many years previously Whitefield had taken periodical trips to America where he enjoyed enormous popularity as a roving evangelist and the elder Shippens had become his familiar friends and admirers.

During his first appearance in America as a young man of twenty-four Whitefield had attracted such crowds by his eloquence in Philadelphia that Benjamin Franklin had thrown the weight of his influence toward raising funds by public subscription for constructing a hall large enough to hold Whitefield's audiences.[2] It was there in the building at Fourth Street near Arch—" one hundred feet long and seventy broad, about the size of Westminster Hall—" that Whitefield in April 1740, according to the well-known story, had charmed from Franklin's pocket all his copper, silver, and golden coins against Franklin's original hard-headed decision to give nothing at all for the establishment of an orphanage in Georgia.[3] The debt of gratitude created in Whitefield's mind by widespread, generous American support of this project brought unexpected returns a dozen years later when the College of New Jersey (later to become Princeton), seeking expansion in the 1750's and thwarted in its schemes for money-raising by Quakers in the Assembly, sent representatives to the British Isles to raise funds.[4] Whitefield saw to it that the statement Governor

---

[1] Tyerman, **2**: 419.
[2] Montgomery, 25.
[3] *Ibid.*, 27.
[4] Tyerman, **2**: 255-256.

Jonathan Belcher of New Jersey had prepared to put before the public the aims of the young American college was printed and then signed by the Countess of Huntingdon, the Reverend Philip Doddridge, and other clergymen of importance as well as by himself. He took pains to give the document wide circulation and preached sermons in favor of New Jersey's college, an institution which he considered vital for the spreading of the gospel in Maryland and Virginia. Doubtless he was as persuasively successful in extracting copper and silver and gold from reluctant English pockets as he had been with Franklin in America. Later support from British dissenters in general resulted from the appeals of two prominent Presbyterian ministers, Samuel Davies and Gilbert Tennent, who spent most of 1754 in England and Scotland raising funds.[5] At the commencement exercises of the College of New Jersey in September, 1754, the Reverend George Whitefield as a distinguished guest received an honorary M. A.[6] According to an English account, this was " a dubious honor " bestowed by the president and trustees " with almost unseemly haste " in exercise of " the powers conferred upon them by the Royal Charter obtained from George II only six years before," but Whitefield in a letter to Selina, Countess of Huntingdon, expressed complete pleasure with the occasion where he encountered " such a number of simple-hearted united ministers [as] I never saw before," and he concluded by outlining his plans for an extended American trip of two thousand miles circuit " to New England, thence to Georgia with return through Virginia."

At these commencement exercises in September, 1754, oddly enough, the Reverend George Whitefield, at thirty-nine, and William Shippen, Jr., at eighteen, became fellow alumni of the College of New Jersey. Shippen's father and Uncle Edward of Lancaster were prominent supporters of the college and Shippen himself was completing four years of academic study with distinction. As class valedictorian he delivered a Latin oration and received the A. B. degree. Mr. Whitefield was impressed by the young speaker. Was it his handsome profile or his fluent Latin which brought forth the comparison to the Roman orators? Praise

[5] Wertenbaker, 32-35.   [6] Tyerman, 2: 333, 334.

from the tongue of George Whitefield was no mean compliment.
Franklin, a shrewd observer of men, had said this preacher with
his outdoor sermons could reach without vocal strain the ears of
30,000 listeners and he admired him for his "integrity, disin-
terestedness and indefatigable zeal in prosecuting every good
work."[7] Whitefield wrought his magic with equal force as occasion offered upon the colliers of Kingswood or upon the aristocrats frequenting the private chapel of the Countess of Huntingdon. It was David Garrick who started the saying that the mere
pronunciation of *Mesopotamia* by Whitefield would reduce his
hearers to tears. Since his eloquent words were usually accompanied by appropriate action there was undoubtedly much entertainment value in Whitefield's emotional discourses. Under all
the circumstances of association it was natural enough that William Shippen, true to his family's custom of church going, should
frequent the Tabernacle at Moorfields during his months in
London, make "Tabernacle friends" and dine with Mr. Whitefield, when the chance came, as by dispensation of Providence.
Calvinism might be a great prop to self-assurance if one could
have the presumption to believe in his own calling and election.
It was certainly a protection against the wiles of the world, the
flesh and the devil.

[7] Carl Van Doren, *Benjamin Franklin*, 136-137, N. Y., Viking, 1938.

Annus Mirabilis, 1759

LONDON church bells were ringing almost constantly that summer of 1759 to celebrate English victories. It was the year above all others for a colonial to be in England.[1] William Shippen was glad to rejoice with the Londoners over British success, but he thought their illuminations " paltry " compared with Philadelphia's. Horace Walpole who had never seen Philadelphia's illuminations was quite satisfied with London's. Writing on August 8 to the Ambassador to Italy, Sir Horace Mann, Walpole reported, " Every house is illuminated, every street has two bonfires, every bonfire has two hundred squibs, and the poor charming moon yonder that never looked so well in her life is not at all minded, but seems only staring out of a great window at the frantic doings all over town." [2]

The Seven Years War (1756-1763), now raging, had grown into a world-wide struggle which it was known would decide the fate of the British Empire and determine the future set-up of the European state system. William Pitt, whose statecraft won him favor as " the Great Commoner," had staked everything to win territory from France. By his strategy of taking the initiative with English forces in every quarter of the globe, he confused and bewildered the French who never knew where the lightning of England's power would strike next. Concentration of French forces at any one place was thus prevented. English aid, eagerly sought in Germany by Frederick the Great as underdog opposed by French, Russian, and Austrian forces, had been undertaken not so much from an altruistic policy of saving Prussia for Frederick as with the self-seeking motive of " winning the Ameri-

[1] Principal sources for this account are Sir Charles Grant Robertson, *Chatham and the British Empire*, London, Hodder and Stoughton, 1946; Basil Williams, *Life of William Pitt, Earl of Chatham*, 2v., London, Longmans Green, 1913, and *The Whig Supremacy*, Oxford, Clarendon Press, 1939; *Cambridge History of the British Empire*, **1**, N. Y., Macmillan, 1929.

[2] Walpole, **4**: 287.

can war in Germany," as Pitt himself phrased it, by thoroughly scaring France. Raids on the French coast by the English meant that the French must safeguard their homeland instead of recklessly carrying out an invasion of England. The prizes Pitt had in view were America and India, but other enterprises must be kept going vigorously to divert the enemy's attention and scatter his forces.

Pitt was to reap a rich harvest of victories in 1759 in justification for his management of the war. George Whitefield's last appearance in Scotland that summer before return to London in late August had been in Edinburgh where he preached a thanksgiving sermon [3] August 12 to celebrate the victory of Prince Ferdinand of Brunswick at Minden.[4] By resourceful action six English infantry regiments had won laurels in this engagement on August 1, bearing the brunt of the battle on the plains of Minden, and ever since that day bearing *Minden* on their colors. Earlier in the season Minden had been preceded by a victory at Guadeloupe. Within the year England would receive from this rich island in the West Indies sugar worth £425,000 to sweeten her tea.

Would the tea come from India? With great issues at stake and no news from either India or America, Pitt confessed he was in suspense all summer. What a strain upon patience to submit to tedious delays, to wait weeks and months for important news in the days before steam-power, electricity, and the aeroplane had transformed communication! The American colonies were six to eight weeks distant by sailing ship, and the voyage to India around the Cape of Good Hope at the mercy of wind and weather took from five months to a year. Near at hand in Germany that summer things went badly. Wedel's reported victory over the Russians at Zullichau turned out to be a defeat. A few days later, at Kunersdorf, Frederick was completely beaten by the Russians, and it was reported he was ready to abdicate or commit suicide. Horace Walpole proposed that England should give him an ap-

---

[3] Whitefield, too impulsive to wait for a royal proclamation, would also preach three thanksgiving sermons in London on Friday, October 19, 1759 (Tyerman, *2*: 422).

[4] " Every good heart is a bonfire for Prince Ferdinand and a funeral pile for the King of Prussia's defeat " was Walpole's comment (Walpole, *4*: 295).

panage, as a younger son, of some hundred thousand [square] miles on the Ohio! Before the summer was over, however, the French fleet was struck in daring manoeuvres by Admiral Boscawen who " found expedients when others found excuses," Pitt said. Off Cape Lagos, Boscawen succeeded in putting out of action half of Choiseul's great fleet under De la Clue before the threatened invasion of England was ready. In America victories ticked off in July at Niagara, Ticonderoga, and Crown Point, and there was September rejoicing in England, but it was October 12 before news, finally arriving from India by special messenger who had been on the way since April 19, could be made public in an Announcement Extraordinary of the *London Gazette*: Madras was invested against the French it was true, but reinforcements were essential; success was slow and expensive.

Two days later, October 14, Pitt received from Quebec a letter from General Wolfe, dated September 2, " despairing as much as heroes can despair." Quebec seemed impregnable. Wolfe believed that " the courage of a handful of brave men should be exerted only when there is some hope of a favourable event." Two days later yet, October 16, another messenger arrived, a month on the way from Canada with the news that Quebec had fallen to the English September 13 and that James Wolfe had died a hero's death in this engagement on the Plains of Abraham above the St. Lawrence.

Another Announcement Extraordinary came immediately from the *London Gazette* on Wednesday, October 17. " The Capital of the French Empire in North America " had fallen. Montcalm, the French commander, had perished as well as Wolfe. " It was a singular affair," Horace Walpole said, " very near what battles should be, in which only the principals suffer." [5] Today a single monument in a little park below the Plains of Abraham overlooking the St. Lawrence at Quebec commemorates the heroism of the two great generals, Wolfe and Montcalm.

In Court circles Wednesday, October 17 was set apart especially as the occasion for His Royal Highness, the Prince of Wales, and the Royal Family with most of the nobility in town to wait

[5] *Ibid.*, 299.

upon His Majesty, at Kensington, " to pay their respects on the joyful news of the taking of Quebec. The Park and Tower guns were fired, flags everywhere displayed from the steeples and the greatest illuminations were made throughout the city and suburbs that were ever known."

" Can one easily leave the remains of such a year as this? " Horace Walpole asked. " It is still all gold. I have not dined or gone to bed by a fire till the day before yesterday. Instead of the glorious and ever-memorable year 1759, as the newspapers call it, I call it this ever-warm and victorious year. We have not had more conquest than fine weather; one would think we had plundered East and West Indies of sunshine. Our bells are worn threadbare with ringing for victories. . . . One thing is very fatiguing, all the world is made knights or generals. Adieu! I don't know a word of news less than the conquest of America." [6]

[6] *Ibid.*, 314.

Anatomy with the Hunters

BY mid-October William Shippen was well versed in the ways of William Hunter's Anatomical School in which John Hunter, the younger of the brothers, was a prime influence.[1] Shippen moved from Southwark to Hunter's house in the Great Piazza, Covent Garden, on Tuesday, October 2, 1759. Dr. Hunter's lectures had begun the day before and dissection started Friday of the same week. It was an absorbing life with discovery awaiting every motion of the scalpel. For fifteen days beginning October 5 the diary mentions little else but dissecting all day. At five o'clock in the afternoon Dr. Hunter's daily lecture began, lasting until half past seven. After supper Shippen often enjoyed the privilege of chatting with Mr. Hunter " upon anatomical points " until bedtime. He dissected assiduously Sundays as well as weekdays and forgot to go to church until October 21. When he had time to relax, he ran to the coffee house to read the newspapers and look for letters or went to the theatre. Drury Lane and Covent Garden theatres were conveniently near by. On October 12 he went to see Garrick in Macbeth; on the fifteenth John Hunter took him to the auction of the late man-midwife Dr. Middleton whose medical library was being offered for sale; on Thursday, October 18, noting his pleasure in the " news of the taking of Quebec, illuminations, etc." he had a varied day attending Hospital in the morning; hearing Mark Akenside's Harveiian oration at two in the afternoon, " very entertaining " at the Royal College of Physicians; back to Covent Garden again at five to listen to Dr. Hunter's lecture.

At five in the afternoon David Garrick was William Hunter's great rival. Drury Lane opened its doors at 5:30 P. M.[2] The

[1] For a complete account upon which this survey is based see *A memoir of John and William Hunter*, by George C. Peachey, Plymouth, England, 1924.
[2] For theatrical data see: D. B. Wyndham Lewis, *The hooded hawk*, N. Y., Longmans Green, 1947; Margaret Barton, *Garrick*, N. Y., Macmillan, 1949; Desmond Shawe-Taylor, *Covent Garden*, N. Y., Chanticleer Press, 1948.

principal play began at 6:30 and was followed by a two-act farce. The only way to get one of the cheap seats was to come early and wait until the scrimmage for entrance began. Drury Lane had a cavernous pit lined on each side by three tiers of boxes, the occupants of which paid several shillings for their seats. Half a crown paid for a good-enough place in the pit or one of the three galleries facing the stage; latecomers could see the second play for a shilling. An orchestra played before the curtain went up what was called the First, Second, and Third Musick. Lighting must have been disappointingly inadequate from a few chandeliers and a row of oil footlights. Since the players could not be well seen overwrought oratorical declamation and over-acting were perhaps necessarily resorted to by the actors to hold attention. The students from the anatomical rooms were in no mood to criticize or complain. After bending over cadavers all day they enjoyed being part of the rowdy crowd and pushing their way to the backless pit benches or crowded galleries, and nobody seemed to object if they smelled of the laboratory. Only Dr. Hunter complained, because of empty seats in his lecture room, but to no avail. During his winter course in 1768 he was finally forced to change the time of his afternoon lecture from 5 o'clock to 2, in order to hold his theatre-loving audience.

Dr. Hunter's ability as a lecturer was so well known even outside the medical profession that it became the custom for outstanding men, particularly fellow Scots, to seek attendance at his introductory lecture given just before dissection started. Later in the century Edmund Burke, Adam Smith, and Edward Gibbon sat among his listeners with admiration. Gibbon, in fact, reported in his letters his constant daily attendance one winter at the two hour sessions of Dr. Hunter's anatomy lectures and could not be induced to leave London that season on any pretext whatsoever since he found the lectures " have opened to me a new and very entertaining scene *within myself*." When the Reverend Alexander Carlyle, the Dean of Inveresk, was admitted with his friend the Scottish historian, William Robertson, by appointment with Hunter to a lecture on the eye, he found himself fascinated by this excursion outside the field of theology and called the lecture

" one of the most elegant, clear and brilliant . . . any of us had ever heard." [3] Could it be, one wonders, that perhaps Laurence Sterne had dropped in to hear Dr. Hunter some day when he was giving an obstetrical discourse? Sterne's *Tristram Shandy* must have caught the eye and interest of William Shippen since it was first published in an installment in 1759, and more fully early in January, 1760. Its fairly accurate technical statements about the force exerted by the pregnant uterus seem astonishing facts for a clergyman to have picked up at random without some medical authority in the background. Although such a visit from Sterne to Hunter is entirely guesswork, such a meeting would have been provocative.

In teaching his young students anatomy William Hunter was able to introduce the Paris method used by less restricted teachers on the continent " providing each of his pupils with one entire body and from time to time inspecting the dissections himself." Popular opposition to the use of dead bodies for dissection continued, but the dissolution of the United Company of Barbers and Surgeons had removed the stigma of illegality from the gathering of subjects for dissection by private teachers. Hunter, high-minded, was no patron of chance resurrectionists. Bodies of criminals and paupers could be secured for his work. Sensitive to public opinion, William Hunter cautioned his pupils against " giving offence to the populace " and advised them to be on their guard, to " speak with caution of what may be passing here, especially with respect to dead bodies." The dissecting rooms were not to be exhibited to strangers who " might chuse to visit us from an idle or even malevolent curiosity."

In addition to making dissections William Shippen and his fellow students practiced operations on cadavers, learned to prepare and mount anatomical and pathological specimens, and were taught the art of injection as developed especially through the skill of John Hunter, his brother's able assistant, who was in

[3] Walpole, *11*: 309; Edward Gibbon, *Private letters of Edward Gibbon*, ed. Prothero, *2*: 302-306, London, 1896 (letters written 1777). Prothero errs in ascribing " Dr. Hunter's Lectures " to John Hunter, who as a surgeon was always known according to English custom as *Mr. Hunter*; Alexander Carlyle, *Autobiography*, 346, Edinburgh, 1860; Jane Oppenheimer, *New aspects of John and William Hunter*, 121, N. Y., H. Schuman, 1946.

charge of the house in the Great Piazza. During the winter of
1758 and the entire summer of 1759 John Hunter was devoting
himself specifically to research into the absorbent vessels which
was only put aside when he developed pneumonia.

The art of anatomical injection,[4] or demonstrating the blood
vessels and other channels and cavities of the animal body by
filling them with colored substances, arose in Holland under
Swammerdam and Ruysch during the latter part of the seventeenth
century and was now reaching a high state of perfection in London
where it was being skillfully and intensively applied by William
and John Hunter and their associates in preparing anatomical
specimens for their museum collections and also for research on
special problems. William Hunter used the injection method in
the researches by which he proved the independence of the fetal
circulation from that of the mother. In this study he was at first
aided by Colin Mackenzie, whose lectures on midwifery Shippen
had attended during the summer of 1759.

The frequent mention of injection work in the diary shows in
what active use this method was at the time of Shippen's residence
with Hunter. The work in which Shippen participated consisted
first in proportioning and mixing the injection fluid, which was
made up of finely powdered pigments such as vermilion, ultra-
marine, etc., suspended in resin, glue, or a fatty substance such as
lard or tallow. A tube (cannula) was then introduced into the
vessel or other channel and tied in place. Through it the injection mass, previously warmed if it was made up with fat or resin,
was forced by a piston-syringe or by gravity flow from a suspended
bottle. The injected structures were exposed by suitable dissection and sketched, or the preparation was preserved in spirits for
study and exhibition. Such work calls for manual dexterity and
presence of mind and the preparations are often of great aesthetic
quality, appealing to the artistic feeling which characterizes most
anatomists and which was strong in Shippen.[5]

Animal experimentation was occasionally attempted, as for
instance on November 3 when Shippen reports laconically " busy

[4] Charles Singer, *Studies in the history of science,* **2,** chap. 7, Oxford, Clarendon
Press, 1921.
[5] Information from GWC.

in opening a Live Dog to see the Lacteals and thoracic Duct etc."
Vivisection, however cruel it seems, was undertaken in this instance to demonstrate something not easily seen in the dead body
and in Shippen's time presenting difficulties for injection. The
lacteals (lymphatic vessels in the mesentery serving to carry lymph
from the small intestines into the thoracic duct, the main channel
of the lymphatic system) could be seen strikingly in this experiment on the living animal which can now be performed under
anaesthesia. When opened after a meal rich in fat, the lacteals
of the dog appeared as white channels in the mesentery glistening
with the milky fat they were conveying from the intestine. Shippen's assigment to study the lymphatic vessels of the dog reflects
William Hunter's great interest in the lymphatic system and fore-
shadows the brilliant work done at Hunter's Anatomy School in
the following decade by Cruikshank and Hewson. Cruikshank
mapped the human lymphatic system in detail and Hewson was
engaged in proving the existence of lymphatic vessels in fishes,
amphibians, and birds during Benjamin Rush's stay in London in
1768, thus upholding the Hunters in their controversy with Haller
as to the function of the lymphatic system.[5]

Shippen's father had planned with forethought that his son
should have this session in London " with the finest Anatomist for
Dissections, Injections &c in England " and " visit the Hospitals
daily to attend Lectures of Midwifery with a Gentleman who will
make that branch as familiar to him as he can want or wish."
Working first with Colin Mackenzie, man-midwife, and then with
John and William Hunter in their school of anatomy, the eager
young man from Philadelphia was receiving the soundest instruction which the eighteenth century could offer in the specialties
which he most wished to cultivate.

William Hunter had come to London about 1740 from Edinburgh where he had studied with Monro and Cullen without
receiving a medical degree. In London he devoted himself to
dissection and midwifery under the instruction of Douglas and
Smellie, the outstanding teachers of these subjects. It was not
until 1746 that with sure mastery of both specialties he set up his
own school where he was to surpass his teachers. In 1748 he was

joined by his young brother John, an unschooled country boy from
Lanarkshire, who more or less by chance " laid down the chisel,
the rule and the mallet of the wheelwright," Jesse Foot said, to
" take up the knife, the blow-torch and probe of his brother, the
anatomist." [6] Hand skill, curiosity, and intelligence combined to
give John Hunter instant success in this strange new field, and
he spent eleven successive winters in the dissecting room, devoting
some summer months to following surgical practice until qualified
to teach surgery. These extraordinary brothers by careful observation and clear-headed reasoning changed the current of eighteenth-
century medical thought. As the years went by, William Hunter,
while directing the affairs of his school of anatomy, devoted more
and more time to his private practice as man-midwife, particularly
after his appointment in 1761 as Physician Extraordinary to Queen
Charlotte. Having " sole direction of Her Majesty's health as a
child-bearing Lady " [7] greatly increased his reputation with people
of wealth and rank and helped to accustom the public to the
desirability and propriety of employing properly qualified physicians for childbirth instead of patronizing midwives. Glasgow
had given William Hunter an M. D. in 1750, in recognition of his
attainments, but it was not until 1756, when he was disfranchised
from his previous surgical connection with the Corporation of
Surgeons and admitted licentiate of the College of Physicians,
that he used the title, Doctor. While William Shippen was a student of anatomy William Hunter was already engrossed in the
preparation of his great folio, *The Anatomy of the Gravid Uterus*,
which after thirty years of devoted effort appeared in 1774, hailed
as an immortal work with its marvelous plates made, most of them,
from drawings by van Rymsdyk from immediate observation of

---

[6] Jesse Foot, *Life of John Hunter*, 10, London, 1794, is quoted by Peachey, 101.

[7] Peachey quotes (p. 114) this descriptive expression of William Hunter's from
a letter which Dr. Hunter wrote to William Cullen in Edinburgh to announce the
birth of the Prince of Wales on August 12, 1762. The Queen was delivered by a
midwife while Dr. Hunter advised from an antechamber. On September 18, 1762
(*London Evening Post* announcement) Dr. William Hunter was appointed Physician Extraordinary to Her Majesty. It is possible that at some time in her later
pregnancies (she had fifteen children) Dr. Hunter himself delivered the Queen.
This would give sanction to the man-midwife; and his employment, spreading from
Court Circles down to the great middle class, would at last become the popular
choice, fashion joining with the increase of knowledge to create custom.

dissections "with no other desire (on the part of the author) than to discover the truth." [8] A modern reader of this volume will find striking evidence of William Hunter's objective judgment in his readiness to discard ideas sanctioned by tradition in favor of what his own dissections and investigations have revealed.

In 1759, when Shippen came to the house in the Great Piazza to study anatomy, William Hunter was living in Jermyn Street where he conducted his private practice. For years it had been his custom to maintain two separate establishments. Before moving to Jermyn Street he had lived in the Little Piazza, reserving the house in the Great Piazza (acquired in 1749 and referred to as "my brother's house" because John made it his home) for dissecting and lecture rooms and quarters for resident students. Establishment of the better known quarters in Great Windmill Street was not made until 1767. Peachey has suggested in a supplement to his excellent *Memoir* that William Hunter already knew that protection of his women patients from possibility of infection demanded that his practice must not be carried on in the same house where dissections were made, thereby anticipating in his thought by almost a hundred years the findings of Oliver Wendell Holmes and Semmelweis as to the transmission of puerperal fever.[9] To corroborate this he states that when William Hunter was in attendance upon Queen Charlotte in 1761-1762 he entirely abandoned anatomical lectures and teaching. A case might equally well be made out to support the theory that William Hunter by the wide separation of anatomical laboratory and consulting room was protecting the women he attended from psychological trauma and their fear of maternal impressions and that he closed his anatomical laboratory in 1761-1762 because of fatigue from overwork in two specialties. The departure of his brother, John, just at this time, on the expedition against Belleisle as staff-surgeon in the British Army certainly left the anatomical part of the enterprise temporarily crippled.

John Hunter left London for Belleisle in March, 1761, and

[8] Henry Russell Andrews, William Hunter and his work in midwifery, *British Med. Jour.*, 1: 277-281, 1915.
[9] George C. Peachey, William Hunter's obstetrical career, *Annals of Med. Hist.*, n. s. 2: 476-479, 1930.

spent approximately two years in army service. Out of this experience came an important book, his *Treatise on the Blood,
Inflammation and Gun-shot Wounds*, 1794. John Hunter was a
more spectacular figure than his older brother and probably a more
profound thinker. William was renowned for suavity of manner,
an asset with patients; John had a choleric temper and the force
which is often its accompaniment. When William Shippen began
dissection in London in October, 1759, " Mr. Hunter " was an
enthusiastic young teacher, only nine years his senior, flushed with
success in his studies on the blood and lymphatic vessels, the structure of the testis, and the anatomy of hernias. Mr. Hunter was not
content with mere observation. He must understand the meaning
of what he saw, know what principles were in operation, what
relationships were involved. Eleven years in the dissecting room
had given him enviable surety in his field which served as a foundation for the surgical ingenuity and dexterity he was soon to
display, particularly in dealing with the treatment of gun-shot
wounds.

It was not only John Hunter's knowledge and skill that won
admiration from his students. Shippen's diary shows that Mr.
Hunter had the knack of taking students into his confidence, of
imparting to them the power of his own enthusiasm, of stimulating tireless activity. He made them feel that they were co-
explorers in solving the problems of human structure. A great
man in the making, he was never too busy after a hard day's
work, we learn from the diary, to talk anatomically with William
Shippen until bedtime. How tantalizing it is that our diarist
makes no attempt to record in detail what he and Mr. Hunter
talked about in these prolonged evening sessions!

In later years John Hunter was to pursue profound and detailed
studies in comparative anatomy and become the foremost physiological anatomist of his day. Anatomy led him naturally to path-
ology where he was a pathfinder. His discoveries found immediate application in the treatment of disease, particularly of disease
requiring surgical intervention. He achieved during his development a scientific point of view which bewildered his conservative
contemporaries. His activities both professional and personal
were branded as " unaccountable." His theories, to say the least,

were considered "extravagant." In 1780, unfortunately, he became at odds with his brother because of a strange dispute they had as to priority of discovery in work done twenty-six years previously, in 1754, with the assistance of the late Colin Mackenzie! This quarrel divided the two brothers for the rest of their lives. Although John was called to attend William in his last illness (after his collapse at his final lecture, 1783), it is said that the professional services were rendered with strict professional attention to the needs of the patient but without any evidence of reconciliation or recognition of the ties of blood that bound them. Ten years later John indulged in his last quarrel at a Board meeting in St. George's Hospital, where a disagreement between him and his colleagues apparently led to a seizure which cost him his life in October 1793.

It is impossible within these limits to do justice to the lives and achievements of John and William Hunter, the outstanding medical biologists of their age, but it is easily seen from the diary kept by the young Philadelphian that their influence profoundly changed William Shippen. He came to their anatomy school as an ambitious boy; he left them as a well-trained man with a purpose. Some of those evening anatomical talks with John Hunter may well have raised the question as to what Shippen would do upon return to America. Perhaps they talked at times of the necessity of establishing medical instruction in such a center as Philadelphia. It is impossible to determine now after almost two hundred years just when the idea of formally organizing a medical school in Philadelphia was broached or by whom. The Hunters were not schoolmen themselves though talented teachers. If William Shippen wished to imitate their accomplishment he would set up as a private teacher in Philadelphia and establish instruction in anatomy with dignity in a school of his own on a high investigative level.

Garrick; and Residence in Covent Garden

SUMMER was merged in autumn; October's golden sunshine was dissolved by November's thick fogs. "Go not out of doors," Horace Walpole advised Lady Hervey. "Gouts and rheumatisms are abroad. Warm clothes, good fires and a room full of pictures, glasses and scarlet damask are the best physic." [1]

Country pleasures were over, the playhouses were open now six nights a week with rapid change of bills to please London's relatively small theatre-going public. David Garrick, approaching forty-three, was looking a little jaded, "for his face had had double the business of any other man's," Dr. Johnson said,[2] but he was still a public idol for many years and Shippen fell under his spell that autumn of 1759. Fatigued as a young man can be after a long day of dissecting or injecting and experimenting, what a relief it was to him to enter the doors of the theatre and lose himself in the realm of fantasy! As to plays performed at this time there were Shakespearian revivals and a large stock of old favorites which had piled up since the reopening of the theatres after the Restoration; there were the comedies written earlier in the century by Steele, Vanbrugh, and Farquhar; there were new plays being constantly submitted by every man who liked to fancy himself a playwright, some of which, like the Reverend James Townley's *High Life Below Stairs*, made an immediate hit.

Garrick's Shakespearian roles were justly famous, though he often used corrupted versions of the tragic and historical plays of Shakespeare, and even tinkered himself with the make-up of Macbeth and Hamlet. Dr. Johnson, rather critical of his fellow

[1] Walpole, 4: 317.
[2] Boswell attributes this remark of Dr. Johnson's to a later period (Boswell's *Johnson*, ed. Ingpen, 1: 558).

74

townsman and ex-pupil whom he had brought to London, and no doubt somewhat envious of Garrick's greater worldly success, told Mrs. Siddons that David was no declaimer. "There was not one of his own scene-shifters who could not have spoken *To be or not to be,* better than he did; yet he was the only actor I ever saw whom I could call a master both of comedy and tragedy; though I liked him best in comedy. A true conception of character and natural expression of it were his distinguished excellencies." [3]

Eighteenth-century audiences delighted in comedy. Shippen saw Garrick in his great roles as Archer in *The Beaux Stratagem* and Ranger in *The Suspicious Husband* with the amusement they always brought. In Garrick's Shakespearian performances he was to find *Macbeth* " surprising" and the terrible force of his *King Lear* " inimitable." Lighter plays predominate in the list of performances seen by the young American visitor during 1759 and noticed by name in his diary. He was fortunate to be in England while the London stage was in the full swing of its power. A list of the plays which Shippen saw during the four months from late September to late January is worth perusing for the light it throws upon the theatrical fare which was amusing Londoners during the winter of 1759. His evenings of theatrical delight and the various plays he saw are listed as follows: [4]

September 26, 1759: *The Beaux Stratagem.* In this comedy of manners by George Farquhar (which has had a recent successful revival in twentieth-century London) Garrick took the leading part as the gentleman footman, Archer, dressed in brilliant light blue and silver livery and wearing a laced hat.

October 2, 1759: *Conscious Lovers* by Richard Steele, a play exposing the follies of duelling in which the Irish actor Thomas King was starring.

October 4, 1759: *The Mourning Bride* with Garrick in the part of Osmyn. This play by William Congreve was greatly admired by Dr. Johnson who thought Congreve's description of the temple was " the finest poetical passage he ever read," exceeding anything produced by Shakespeare.

October 12, 1759: *Macbeth* with Garrick in the title role, wearing " a

[3] *Ibid.,* 2: 1030-1031.

[4] For complete documentation see Genest, 4: 574-591. Supplementary information from Percy Fitzgerald, *The life of David Garrick,* London, 1878; Margaret Barton, *Garrick,* N. Y., Macmillan, 1949; D. B. Wyndham Lewis, *The hooded hawk,* N. Y., Longmans Green, 1947; Austin Dobson, 1, 2, 3; Walpole, 4.

scarlet coat like a military officer, a waistcoast laced with silver, and a wig and breeches of the cut of the time." Garrick had planned to play Macbeth as written by Shakespeare, discarding the changes and additions by Davenant which had crept into common use, but he could not resist adding certain explanatory passages of his own and a long dying speech which gave him opportunity to have an effective death upon the stage.

October 17, 1759: *Isabella, or The Fatal Marriage* by Thomas Southerne, an adaptation of Aphra Behn's *The Nun or The Fair Vow-Breaker*, with some borrowings from Boccaccio's *Decameron*. Garrick and Mrs. Cibber played respectively the parts of Biron and Isabella.

October 29, 1759: *The Confederacy* by Sir John Vanbrugh. In spite of Garrick's acting the reviewer of *The London Chronicle*, November 3-6, 1759 called this " a dull, nay I may say a disagreeable entertainment."

November 2, 1759: *High Life Below Stairs* was a brilliant new farce, said to have been written by the Reverend James Townley. It had small literary merit but Dr. Johnson found it " really very diverting " when acted and George Selwyn liked the title because he said he was weary of *low* life *above* stairs.

November 10, 1759: *King Lear* with Garrick in the title role. Although Horace Walpole disparaged this presentation it won general praise as the finest interpretation yet seen upon the stage. Shakespeare's original texts were at that time unfamiliar except to students of literature and eighteenth century audiences did not therefore realize that various changes including the addition of a happy ending by Nahum Tate had reduced the tragedy " to the comfortable dimensions of a melodrama " (see Margaret Barton, *Garrick*, 44-47).

November 20, 1759: *A Woman's A Riddle*, nominally by Christopher Bullock who put it on the stage, is actually a translation of a Spanish comedy, *La Dama Duende*. This performance was a revival of a play not seen for a quarter of a century.

November 23, 1759: *Comus, A Masque* adapted from Milton by Dr. Dalton with music by Thomas Arne was received with delight at every performance. Dr. Arne's exquisite music must have contributed greatly to its success. Mrs. Cibber took the part of the Lady. The elevated character of this production contrasts sharply with the boisterous comedies liked by eighteenth-century audiences.

December 6, 1759: *Oroonoko* with Garrick in two roles, that of Oroonoko, the hero, and the smaller part of Aboan who stabs himself and dies upon the stage. Mrs. Cibber was again Garrick's leading lady as Imoinda. The plot had been taken from Aphra Behn's novel of the same name.

December 12, 1759: Shippen saw a shilling's worth of *The Merchant of Venice*! Dr. Hunter's late afternoon lecture " from 5 to 7½ " had kept him from seeing the whole performance in which Charles Macklin played inimitably as Shylock. It is interesting to note that Macklin's Shylock brought him laurels for more than forty years until his farewell performance at the age of ninety-nine in Covent Garden, 1789. Macklin was moreover a versatile actor and on this particular December evening Shippen had the good fortune to see him also in *Love a la Môde*, a farce of Macklin's own devising in which he played the part of an Irish officer, Sir Archy McSarcasm.

December 14, 1759: *The Tutor*, a new burletta, taken from the Italian was withdrawn after one performance and never printed. Another version made in 1765 was also unsuccessful.

December 19, 1759: *The Refusal* or *The Ladies' Philosopher* by Colley Cibber derived from Moliere's *Les Femmes Scavantes*. This play ran only six nights but Macklin's performance as Sir Gilbert was called brilliant. The plot made use of the follies and infatuations attending the South Sea bubble investments.

January   4, 1760 ⎱ *Benefits for the Sufferers in the King Street Fire,*
January 16, 1760 ⎰   December 23, 1759 (see diary).

On January 4 Shippen went to an unnamed play (p. 33) with T. Francis. Perhaps they attended the benefit performance of Congreve's *Mourning Bride* with Gentleman Smith as Osmyn. The second benefit, January 16, presented at Drury Lane was a performance of Mrs. Centlivre's comedy, *The Wonder, A Woman Keeps A Secret.* This was a favorite play of Garrick's in which he took the part of Don Felix and which was indeed his selection years later in 1775 when he made his last "final appearance" before retirement from the stage. Shippen unfortunately missed this performance on January 16 when he was "writing all day till lecture."

January 17, 1760: *The Suspicious Husband* by Dr. Benjamin Hoadley. Garrick as Ranger in this comedy always delighted his audiences.

January 19, 1760: "*Comus* [5] at C. G." is the last play listed in the diary.[6]

If Uncle Edward of Lancaster could have been transported to

[5] Milton's austere morality play was transformed by Dalton into an elaborate and elegant eighteenth-century pantomime. In this arrangement of *Comus* Dr. Thomas Arne's ability as a lyric composer was first recognized in its earliest performances in 1739. The revival of performances twenty years later in 1759 was perhaps in tribute to Dr. Arne who received that year an honorary degree in music from Oxford University (Herbert Langley, *Doctor Arne*, 19-25, Cambridge, The Univ. Press; 1938; Brother Burnham W. Horner, *The life and works of Dr. Arne 1710-1778*, 7, London, Chiswick Press, 1893; Genest, 4: 590; BD, 2: 117).

[6] Since dramatic records of the eighteenth century have usually been assembled from manuscript lists compiled without cognizance of any last minute substitutions which often have to be made in the theatre, it is not strange that Genest and Shippen do not in every case agree as to the exact dates of the performances which have been listed.

Covent Garden during the theatre season he would have felt that all his cautions to his nephew against rakes and fops and their mopsies had been justified. This region, once a simple convent garden where the nightingales sang to the good brothers of the ancient Abbey of Westminster in the loveliness of an English spring, had become a place of fashionable residence in the seventeenth century. A square had been laid out [7] and to surround it great arcades, or piazzas, had been planned by Inigo Jones who also designed St. Paul's Church on the west side of the Market. Only two sides of the arcades had been finished but great houses had been built for the Earl of Bedford, Lord Orford, and other aristocrats. Bishop Berkeley and Sir Kenelm Digby and many other notables had lived there, but early in the eighteenth century the nobility and gentry had all moved to the west of town, leaving Covent Garden to the tradesmen and the bohemians. The market had pushed its way into the center of the square, shops, coffee houses, taverns, supper clubs, brothels, gaming houses, and bagnios (so-called bathing houses), sprang up to create a night life of unrestricted gaiety. After the theatre there swarmed the streets a crowd whose elements suggested that a multiplied cast of *The Beggar's Opera* had been let loose to ply their trades.

Rents had fallen with the neighborhood's reputation for sobriety, so that Dr. Hunter probably got his fine house in this center of wickedness for a song when he needed it in 1749. The large, high-ceilinged rooms of the house he secured at the northwest corner of the Great Piazza (next door to the mansion Lord Orford had occupied which became later the National Sporting Club) [8] proved excellent for his purposes and he was able to transform them into very acceptable laboratory quarters. Upstairs there was space for his young medical men to live. Artists and literary men sought this neighborhood, too, liking its air of past luxury, and naturally it attracted stage people because of its proximity to the theatres. Garrick lived for a time in King Street

---

[7] Austin Dobson, 3: 324-346; Desmond Shawe-Taylor, *Covent Garden*, 9-15, N. Y., Chanticleer Press, 1948.

[8] The site of Hunter's house has been confirmed by Mr. W. R. Le Fanu, Librarian of the Royal College of Surgeons, London, as the "western-most on the north side of the Great Piazza."

and Charles Macklin tried running a tavern of his own in the neighborhood. Kitty Clive had adorned Henrietta Street. Nearby Tom Davies, whose life of Garrick appeared in 1780, had his bookshop in Russell Street, and it was there in his back-parlor that he introduced Boswell to Johnson in the spring of 1763.

The elder Shippens need not have worried about the company young William would keep. He was fastidious and discriminating. The diversions of an English summer brought him many country excursions and desirable companionship on horseback rides and coaching parties while he grew familiar with the charms of the English landscape. He accepted invitations to dances where no doubt all the girls he met considered the young American with his good looks a great catch. He found these English girls not only pretty but "genteel" and "elegantly dressed" in the "flounced Trollopes" young ladies of fashion affected in the 50's and 60's of the eighteenth century. Loving music, he was attracted by Miss Jefferys, "agreable and chatty," who could sing with him while John Latham played the German flute. In the Latham household in Peckham he made the acquaintance of a doctor's family "most like my Father's of any I have met with in England, 3 boys and 1 spoilt girl like Sukey." He was astonished at the ability of Master Latham who though only eight years old could "play the fiddle very well though never taught by any Body." The evening hours slipped away all too quickly in Peckham while young John and William and the elder Latham talked medically and put away their bottles of claret. In the autumn an old school-fellow, Gerardus Clarkson, arrived in London in the course of an extended tour of medical centers, and Shippen showed him the town. Some cranberries and apples had been sent by ship from America and an accommodating housekeeper must have taken the trouble to concoct some dainties for the young men. Shippen and Clarkson feasted in the Great Piazza one evening on "Philadelphia cranberry Pye, very fine," and after spending Christmas Day together enjoyed "Mincepyes" in Shippen's rooms. How little these young medical students foresaw what the future would bring them in mature manhood! John Latham, described by Shippen that summer as "a worthy lad" studying at Guy's, would become known at Dartford where he practiced many years as an excellent physician and would acquire a considerable fortune, but he would gradually succumb to the spell of country life, become the close associate of Thomas Pennant and his collaborator, achieve election to the Royal Society and surprise everybody in his old age by producing at eighty-one an authoritative work on ornithology in eleven volumes with beautiful illustrations designed, etched, and colored by himself. Gerardus Clarkson's future would be that of a greatly loved and respected citizen and physician in Philadelphia and a leader in St. Peter's Episcopal Church. William Shippen would make a name for himself as a hardworking, devoted teacher of obstetrics and anatomy in the College of Philadelphia, later to become the University of Pennsylvania. By transplanting from English to American soil the Hunterian standards in anatomy and obstetrics he would play a leading part in the establishment of medical education in America.

As a young man Shippen evidently attracted attention in England with his handsome chiseled features shown in the later portrait by Gilbert Stuart. Even the gruff Mark Akenside, disliked and caricatured for bearish ways with patients and colleagues, became " kind and judicious " on rounds with William Shippen at St. Thomas's. In compliment to the young man's easy social grace his company was much sought. Visitors from America were numerous in London that summer of 1759. The very first entry in the diary mentions a supper party in July with Acting-Governor James Hamilton of Pennsylvania and the Reverend William Smith, the thirty-two year old Provost of the College of Philadelphia, who had received an Oxford doctorate in March. When winter came a dinner party which Shippen particularly enjoyed took place at the house of Georges René Aufrère in Chelsea. Mr. Aufrère, a man of large fortune, whose firm had constant dealings in America, was assembling one of the finest private art collections in England with the advice of Sir Joshua Reynolds, and his house was full of paintings and statuary.[9] His wideawake wife, interested in public affairs, was a niece of the Countess of Exeter, and her account of Mr. Pitt speaking in November at the House of

[9] Charles Poyntz Stewart, History of the Aufrères, *Proc. Huguenot Soc. of London*, **9**: 145-160, 1911.

Commons in tribute to General Wolfe's heroism at Quebec fascinated Shippen who found her " the most sensible, agreable woman
I ever saw." On another occasion Shippen was the guest of
Thomas Penn who had succeeded to the provincial governmental
duties of the illustrious " Founder," his father. Thomas Penn
had lived for ten years at an earlier period at Bush Hill in Philadelphia, but now he had a town house in New Spring Gardens
near Charing Cross, and it was there that Shippen met Penn's wife,
the charming Lady Juliana, a woman of thirty, much younger
than her husband, and their niece, *Philadelphia* Hannah Freame, a
girl of nineteen, who had been born in America. Tench Francis,
successful American financier, very close to the Penns as their
agent in Pennsylvania, was in London that winter, and looked
up Shippen, as kinsman and fellow townsman, took him to a play
and out to supper. " Cousin Sterling," a young woman about his
own age needed his medical advice. Born Dorothy Willing, she
had come to live in London not long ago as the wife of Captain,
afterwards Sir, Walter Sterling of the Royal Navy. Her husband
had been called to sea on the 40-gun cruiser *Lynn*, and her bachelor
uncle, Mr. Thomas Willing, a director of the Bank of England,
was concerned about her health. The young man found it flattering to be consulted. Most flattering of all attentions were two
invitations in January 1760 from Benjamin Franklin. On Thursday, January 3 they went together to the Royal Society. What a
pair they made as they set out together that evening—the discur-
sive worldly-wise scientist-philosopher-statesman and the handsome young colonial, student of a concentrated discipline! London
streets were distressingly dark, but the approach to the Royal
Society in Crane Court was illuminated, through Newton's still
effective order, by a lamp hung out on meeting nights above the
entrance to the Court from Fleet Street, symbolic as well as practical in its shining. Going to the Royal Society was a rare favor,
but the really unforgetable occasion for a young man came on
Twelfth Night, January 6, when Franklin took Shippen to Court
to see the Royal Family. They were out together until two in the
morning, and Shippen lost his hat in the midst of " the greatest
and best mob I ever saw."

For some time there has been little mention of evangelical

friends in the diary.   His Majesty George II had appointed a
Thanksgiving Day for victories vouchsafed the English, and by
chance the day selected was Thursday, November 27, 1759, the
last Thursday in November, later to become the annual Thanksgiving Day for mercies in America.   William Shippen spent the
day with the De Berdts and all went to hear George Whitefield's
Thanksgiving sermon in the Tabernacle.   Shippen was at church
again December 2 and December 9, but on the sixteenth he had
Sunday dinner with the Penns who now belonged to the Church
of England.   On December 23 he was again the guest of the
De Berdt's and probably went to church though he does not mention it.   On Sunday, December 30, the De Berdts have him bleeding twelve-year-old Esther; he dines with the parents and hears
the famous Mr. Edwards preach.   Sunday January 6 he is otherwise engaged with Mr. Franklin, and indeed there are no entries
after that until January 14.   The De Berdts have him in line for
church the following Sunday.   The preacher was James Fordyce,
and Shippen finds him " an affected stiff orator " on January 20.
This page of the diary is smeared, some words have been effaced,
the last entry in the book is made January 22.

   Shippen's diary noted that the autumn course of Dr. Hunter's
lectures closed on January 3, 1760.   The winter lectures began
January 14.   An active program in the laboratories will continue
until their close late in the spring.   Shippen is no longer planning
to go to the continent to study in Leyden and France.   War between England and France prevents the realization of such a plan
but there is another reason for a change.   The Hunters, Colin
Mackenzie, and Dr. Fothergill all think that Edinburgh is the
only place to obtain thorough theoretical grounding from the
really great faculty which that north-British institution has assembled in its medical school where the Monros and William Cullen
are distinguished teachers and investigators.

   John and William Hunter have become William Shippen's
guiding stars in a world of reality and fact.   His whole philosophy
is changing and with it the influence of George Whitefield is
waning.   A lifetime will give Shippen little enough time, he sees,
to accomplish his purposes as a medical teacher and a practitioner.
He will " do good and pursue it," but that goading sense of sin,

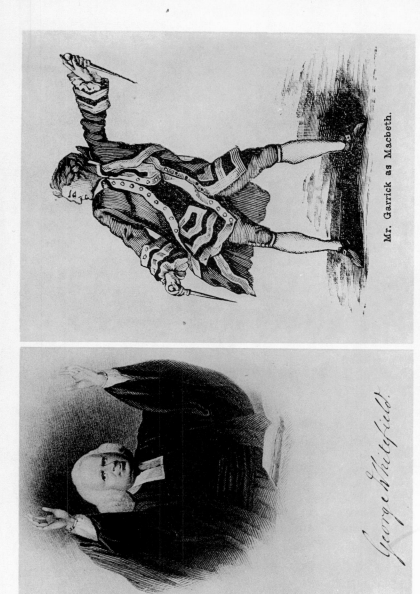

Mr. Garrick as Macbeth.

George Whitefield.

Fig. 5. Whitefield and Garrick as Shippen saw them.

Fig. 6. Supposed Portrait of John Hunter in early maturity.

that need for salvation, that system of rewards and punishments in an unknown hereafter begin to seem, perhaps, to his rational mind somewhat like the famous Fordyce preaching, " stiff and affected," or at least an artificial man-made scheme to explain the inexplicable great questions surrounding life and death. His evangelical friends seem somewhat worried about what they no doubt consider his increasing worldliness. He is often with the De Berdts but in his whole diary he never says he likes them.

About this time, while Garrick is becoming the hero of Shippen's leisure and he is going to the theatre as often as he has time and money, Whitefield began to denounce the stage.

Late in 1759 George Whitefield preached a sermon against theatre-going which " stirred a nest of hornets." [10] Almost at once a sixpenny pamphlet appeared in reply. The writer of this pamphlet professed to be a Methodist who had long entertained an "ignorant zeal," he said against theatres but who had been cured of his blind prejudice by meeting a sensible comedian and more than all else by the experience of seeing Garrick act. In consequence he felt that he must denounce the sermon " delivered in a very copious and affecting manner by a certain popular Preacher " because it " threatened attendants of the theatre with damnation." This pamphlet attracted the attention of the *Monthly Review* which, taking the " Discourse of the Theatre-going Methodist " for a text, commented on the affair in these words, " We hope the pious orator, Mr. Whitefield, made some reserve in favor of those who frequent the theatres in the neighborhood of Moorfields, Tottenham Court, Cow Cross and Broad St. Giles.[11] But after all, it were no wonder that a Whitefield, or a Wesley, should be jealous of so powerful a rival as a Garrick, or even of a Woodward, a Shuter or a Yates. However, it must be allowed uncharitable in any performers or managers thus to consign each other's audiences to the devil. We hope our good friends of Drury Lane and Covent Garden have never been chargeable with such unfair and unChristian dealings. . . . Neither decency nor honesty will allow us to break the windows or frighten away the customers of *our rivals in trade.*"

[10] Tyerman, 2: 423 ff.
[11] Gathering places of the followers of Whitefield and Wesley for worship.

Samuel Foote, the dramatist, took wicked delight in the situation by burlesquing Whitefield in a topical play. His merciless comedy, entitled *The Minor*, first acted in Dublin in January, 1760, was ready in July for its London production at the New Theatre in the Haymarket.[12] Whitefield was caricatured as Dr. Squintum, and Foote probably intended that characters called Shift, Smirk, and Mrs. Cole should call to mind other evangelical leaders.

Ministers were quick to denounce this play from their pulpits. Martin Madan,[13] true to Calvinistic principles, disguising himself under the signature Anti-Profanus, published *A Letter to David Garrick*, expostulating against Foote's play which he said should not be styled a comedy but *A Dramatic Libel Against the Christian Religion*. Though it was vile stuff, coarse as well as libelous, the Haymarket was swarming with crowds who came to see it night after night. Other scurrilous plays ridiculing the Methodists soon appeared, some of them so bad they were immediately suppressed. Ballad makers took up the subject readily and their broadsides were scattered all over the streets and parks.

The Countess of Huntingdon was so incensed by what had happened that she called on the Duke of Devonshire, Lord Chamberlain, asking for withdrawal of *The Minor* from performance. Her request failed. Deeply injured, she then went to Garrick who professed to be offended by the play, but it was not long before it was drawing crowds to Drury Lane.[14] The *Monthly Review*, no friend to the Evangelicals, deplored the production. Foote's admirers claimed that this comedy was his cleverest work, and Foote himself in the published version of *The Minor* insisted in his introduction that the only way to cure the Methodists of their madness was by ridicule, an "antidote to their pernicious poison." [15]

---

[12] Genest, 4: 599-600.

[13] His pamphlet ran to 48 pages (Tyerman, 2: 434). Madan was cousin to William Cowper, the poet. Madan's later advocacy of polygamy in his book *Thelyphthora* (1780) cost him his chaplaincy of Lock Hospital (DNB).

[14] Garrick seems to have insisted upon removal of some of the play's vulgarities. One of Mrs. Cole's "unspeakable passages" was made to read: "Dr. Squintum washed me with the soap-suds and scouring sand of the Tabernacle and I became as clean and bright as a pewter platter" (Tyerman, 2: 433).

[15] Foote himself took the parts of Shift, Smirk, and Mrs. Cole, exercising his extraordinary powers of mimicry (Genest, 4: 599-600). The war of the pam-

Did Whitefield enjoy the excitement he had created? He had long been abused by clergymen in England, Scotland, and America, by noisy pamphleteers, both learned and illiterate, by violent mobs. Now he was ridiculed by comedians and their supporters who were ribald and profane. While the controversy raged Whitefield never murmured nor complained; Garrick kept on with his art and Shippen with his play-going.

phleteers raged for months. In August 1760 an anonymous "Minister of the Church of Christ" published *Christian and Critical Remarks exposing the Blasphemy, Falsehood and Scurrility of* The Minor, in 41 pages. Foote himself answered this attack in 41 pages of his own which William Cooke later incorporated in his *Memoirs of Samuel Foote*, 3: 160-201, London, 1805.

Of Fevers and Friendships; Medicine in Scotland

IN addition to the special problems presented by anatomy and obstetrics there was much else in British medicine to interest an active-minded young man during the years of Shippen's sojourn in London and Edinburgh. The study of epidemic fevers, for example, was a subject of great concern. In Edinburgh Shippen was to listen to lectures by William Cullen whose doctrine of nervous excitability as the cause of fever was the great theoretical contribution of the period and was to become a basis of contention between Benjamin Rush and the other Philadelphia doctors three decades later. In London Shippen was already benefiting from the counsel of John Fothergill, the great Quaker internist, whose contribution to the diagnosis and treatment of epidemic fevers was as practical and independently constructive as Cullen's was theoretical and provocative.[1] There were plenty of epidemic fevers in London during the chill winters Shippen spent there submerged in anatomy.

Horace Walpole found the winter of 1760 the bleakest of all seasons when he went to Strawberry Hill in January to tend his goldfish and orange trees. "You cannot figure a duller season," he wrote to his friend, Sir Horace Mann, "The weather bitter, no party, little money, half the world playing the fool in the country, others raising regiments or with their regiments; in short the end of a war and of a reign furnish few episodes." Walpole was worried because Sir Horace Mann was complaining of headaches, but he wisely refused to commit himself when asked by Sir Horace as to the value of Joshua Ward's medicine. "The cures he does in that complaint," he explains, "are done by him in person. He rubs his hand with some preparation and holds it upon

---

[1] Rush, *Autobiography*, ed. Corner, Appendix I; 361-365.

the forehead, from which several found instant relief. If you please I will consult him whether he will send you any preparation for it; but you must first send me the exact symptoms and circumstances of your disorder and constitution, for I would not for the world venture to transmit to you a blind remedy for an unexamined complaint." [2]

This strongly rational point of view was exceptional in an age when there was little general understanding of how to maintain health. Many secrets of basic science which would bring hope to the ill awaited the research of later centuries. While death took tremendous toll of life the doctors were often baffled and the uninformed clung to magic and longed for miracles of healing as in every age.

There was a severe outbreak of sore throats in London that winter. Walpole let his wit play upon the situation. "Whether you are a horse or a man," he wrote, "you are equally in danger. All the horses in town are laid up with sore throats and colds and are so hoarse you cannot hear them speak." [3] He himself was laid up "with a nervous fever these six or seven weeks every night" for which he had "taken enough bark to make a rind for Daphne." There was "cruel havoc" among his friends. The weather continued bitter; the streets were abandoned; the Thames was almost solid.

"A horrid scene of distress" beset the family of Cavendish. "The Duke's sister, Lady Besborough died . . . of the same sore throat of which she lost four children four years ago," Walpole continued. "It looks as if it was a plague fixed in the walls of their house; it broke out again among their servants and carried off two, a year and half after their children. About ten days ago Lord Besborough was seized with it and escaped with difficulty; then the eldest daughter had it though slightly; my Lady attending them is dead in three days. It is the same sore throat which

[2] Walpole, 4: 343-344.
[3] *Ibid.*, 345. Perhaps there is more than one pun (hoarse, horse) intended here. "Whether you are a *horse* or a *man*" may have been a pun Walpole didn't dare to write his friend *Horace Mann*, but used instead, chuckling to himself, when penning a letter to George Montagu. Letters written by Walpole in the early winter of 1759-60 emphasize the widespread prevalence of "contagious sore-throat."

carried off Mr. Pelham's two fine sons, two daughters and a daughter of the Duke of Rutland, at once. The physicians, I think, don't know what to make of it." My Lady Granby, afflicted likewise, and Lavinia Fenton, the Duchess of Bolton (remembered as the original Polly Peachum of *The Beggar's Opera*), died at this time. "Poor Lady Coventry is near completing this black list." [2, 3]

London had suffered from previous outbreaks of so-called "malignant sore throat" in 1747 and 1748. Others were dreaded and would come. Varying symptoms would gain the scrutiny and study of many able minds among physicians as the outbreaks occurred. Dr. John Fothergill had already studied the epidemic which broke out in the warm dry autumns of 1747 and 1748. His observations, recorded in *An Account of the Sore Throat Attended with Ulcers* (1748), attracted attention by his advocacy of a stimulative rather than a depleting treatment. He found bleeding "prejudicial" and heavy purging weakening. He stressed the need of "free air" while the patient was kept warm in bed, cleanliness, and a liquid diet. There should be no forcible scarification of the tonsils. His use of blisters, bark, and opium was moderate. His little book was a model of clinical description but it roused his conservative contemporaries to a storm of criticism. The particular disease Dr. Fothergill was describing was accompanied by the appearance, usually on the second day, of "a skin eruption of deep erysipelatous appearance." Dr. Heberden and later medical authorities seem to have agreed in general that the disease was probably a type of "that variable infectious disease which we know as scarlatina." At this period diphtheria in its pharyngeal form was seldom encountered in England although it seems probable from various early accounts that there had been outbreaks on the continent and in the American colonies. Croup occurred, and was sometimes epidemic, but this was a laryngeal disorder. Outbreaks of tonsillitis were common; some assumed an aberrant form of great severity. In their onset many of these diseases produced similar symptoms and were doubtless sometimes confused. The difficulty of diagnosing such diseases in historical retrospect is so great that R. Hingston Fox, Fothergill's biographer, has even advanced the theory that "there is some evidence for belief that in Fothergill's time diseases of the fauces were in process of evolution, and that out of various epidemic types, one of which he so carefully described, the specific disorders well known to us have been developed." Futile and inconclusive as it is to diagnose a disease almost two hundred years after its occurrence, the outbreak of 1760, as described by Horace Walpole, sounds like what we now call streptococcus sore throat.[4] Influenza, generally known at this time in England as epidemic catarrh or *febris catarrhalis*, was characteristically different in its symptomatology. Epidemic in England in 1762, 1775, and 1782, this disease, too, was made the subject of carefully detailed study by John Fothergill.[5]

Recognition of Dr. Fothergill's skill brought him one of the largest medical practices in London for more than thirty years. He was a public-spirited citizen as well; a well-to-do bachelor who devoted his leisure from domestic cares to philanthropies as a realistic humanitarian working for prison reform and the freedom of negro slaves. For relaxation he indulged himself in the cultivation of wide scientific interests, particularly botany. His circle of influence extended even to America. As a Quaker, valued by English Friends for his counsels, the Quaker colony established by the English in Pennsylvania had become especially dear to his heart. No Englishman of the period had become better known in Philadelphia than Dr. Fothergill whose friends and correspondents included Israel and James Pemberton, Dr. Thomas Bond, the Bartrams, father and son,[6] and Benjamin Franklin. The able young men who came over from the colonies to study medicine in England and in Scotland (where most of them eventually went by his advice to the medical school in Edinburgh) were welcomed and entertained at his town house in Bloomsbury. In his extensive gardens and hothouses at Upton they were taken to see his

[4] R. Hingston Fox, *Dr. John Fothergill and his friends, Chapters in eighteenth century life*, 49-52, London, Macmillan, 1919.

[5] *Ibid.*, 70-72.

[6] The relationships between Peter Collinson and John Bartram and between Dr. Fothergill and William Bartram are traced in pleasant detail by R. Hingston Fox in chapters XIII and XIV of his Fothergill biography.

expanding collection of exotic but "useful" plants which John Bartram had helped him assemble from all over the world. These young students who eagerly sought his professional advice about their education gave him in return first-hand reports from the colonies. He was especially pleased with news which Shippen gave him concerning the Pennsylvania Hospital which Thomas Bond, whom he had known as a student in England, had been instrumental in establishing in 1752.[7] He often talked with William Shippen, and later with John Morgan and Benjamin Rush, about the future growth and medical needs of America. The establishment of a medical school in Philadelphia seemed to him imperative.

In January 1760 William Shippen began his last months of work in anatomy and obstetrics in Dr. Hunter's Great Piazza school. John Hunter had succumbed to illness, a disturbing pneumonia, after eleven confining years in the dissecting rooms, and William Hewson, a leading pupil, succeeded him as instructor in anatomy.[8] After January 22 there is no diary to serve as guide to Shippen's activities but it was customary for Hunter's spring course of lectures to continue until late April or mid-May when warm weather put an end to dissection from lack of proper preservatives. It was this same spring that John Morgan graduated from the College of Philadelphia (May 10) and a few weeks later made his appearance in London for medical studies. Shippen and Morgan had been schoolmates at Dr. Finley's academy in West Nottingham, and they were destined for a future of even closer association as America's medical educators. Well before the opening of the autumn courses in the medical department of the University of Edinburgh in 1760, Shippen had made the necessary transfer from England to Scotland. He spent the following year in theoretical study at the University and in careful preparation of his thesis. The coveted M. D. became his on September 16, 1761, upon presentation of his dissertation *De Placentae cum Utero nexu* which was published soon afterwards. His experience and skill

---

[7] Dr. Fothergill's initial interest in the Pennsylvania Hospital is attributed by Morton (p. 345) to his acquaintance with Dr. William Shippen, Jr., the elder Dr. Shippen being at that time one of the managers of the new institution.

[8] Peachey, 112, 113.

in anatomy had won favorable attention and he had profited from association and study with the Monros, William Cullen, John Hope, and the lesser lights of the great faculty built up by the medical school of the University of Edinburgh.

While William Shippen was perfecting his medical education in Scotland, his cousin Joseph came to England to spend several months. Joseph Shippen, who had distinguished himself at Fort Duquesne for spirited military leadership, was looking forward to peacetime occupation as one of Philadelphia's importers, and he was now surveying European markets and making acquaintance with mercantile houses and their directors. From London he wrote to his father in Lancaster (January 23, 1761): [9]

" Cousin Billey Shippen is at Edinburgh hearing lectures; he is much esteemed there by his Acquaintances and by his Application and the Progress he has made bids fair to make a Figure in his Profession. I hope to see him before I leave England as he is expected here in the Spring."

But in the spring it was the same story. Pushing through to the last stages of his thesis in Edinburgh " Billey " was delayed again. In a letter written April 11 [10] Joseph told his father:

" My cousin Dr. Shippen is still in Scotland and writes me that he can't possibly be in London till July, as he must stay to receive the Feather of M. D. in his Cap, so I'm afraid I shan't see him in this glorious country."

When July came Joseph Shippen embarked from England homeward bound, but it was not until September that William Shippen was able to leave Edinburgh with his degree. In a letter full of public and private gossip John Morgan, writing from London, was pleased to announce to the now absent Joseph that his cousin Dr. Shippen had at last reached the English capital.[11] Morgan had shared in the prevailing excitement in Britain over various changes in the royal household. There had been a royal marriage on September 8 and a coronation two weeks later.

Early in September Charlotte of Mecklenburg had arrived with

[9] Joseph Shippen, Jr. in his letter to his father, Edward of Lancaster. Shippen Papers (HSP) in letter book of Joseph Shippen, Jr.
[10] Same source.
[11] John Morgan's letters to Joseph Shippen in Morgan Papers (HSP).

her attendants in London for her marriage with George III.   The
wedding took place the very next day.   Horace Walpole took
delight in describing the ceremony and the appearance of the
Queen " in white and silver with an endless mantle of violet-
coloured velvet lined with ermine and . . . on her head a beautiful little tiara of diamonds."   The magnificence of the wedding
was eclipsed by the Coronation on September 22.   " Oh! the buzz,
the prattle, the noise, the hurry!   The multitudes . . . guards and
processions made Palace Yard the liveliest spectacle in the
world." [12]   By great good fortune, John Morgan's letter to Joseph
Shippen relates: " Dr. Shippen (who arrived from Scotland but
the day before) [13] and myself with a couple of Ladies were happy
to have a good sight of the Procession, just opposite to Westminster Hall which it came out of.   It is impossible by words to
give any idea of the richness of the Coronation Robes of the King,
the Queen, the Peers and Peeresses or of the august appearance
they all made—nothing could exceed it.   I don't remember on
any occasion to have seen one fourth of the number of people
that had crowded together that day to get a sight of it.   The
Queen is rather a little woman than otherwise, her Face not remarkably handsome, but has great sweetness and affability in her
Looks—a fine slender Waste, her carriage, air and manners incom-
parably easy and genteel."   The King is quite forgotten by John
Morgan.

The Coronation, with its blaze of lights, gorgeous procession,
and unprecedented crowds which excited most spectators, fatigued
Horace Walpole.   " If I was to entitle ages," he wrote, " I would
call this the *century of crowds*."   And again—" Well it was
delightful but not half so charming as its being over."   It was a
mere puppet show, he thought, and it cost a million.   " What is
the finest sight in the world? " he asked.   " A Coronation.   What
do people talk most about?   A Coronation.   What is delightful to
have passed?   A Coronation.   Indeed one has need to be a handsome young Peeress not to be fatigued to death with it." [14]

Shippen had made unusually good time arriving from Scotland

[12] Walpole, **5**: 105-110.
[13] John Morgan's letter to Joseph Shippen, Morgan Papers (HSP).
[14] Walpole, **5**: 110, 119, 121.

for this event. His thesis bears the date of September 16 as the day of its presentation and he is in London September 21 by John Morgan's account, having arrived " but the day before " the Coronation. Morgan and Shippen had before them long careers of rivalry and contention. Their paths crossed and recrossed many times. Now they would separate. Morgan would follow Shippen as a student in Edinburgh as he had followed him in London, but at the University of Edinburgh he would spend twice as much time as Shippen, in two years of study rather than one.

Shippen's education in Great Britain was the exact reverse of that pursued by John Morgan, Samuel Bard of New York, and Benjamin Rush, all of whom at much the same period spent the major part of their time while students in Britain in theoretical studies at Edinburgh, allotting a much shorter time to practical work in anatomy and hospital observation in London. This, to be sure, denotes the fundamental difference in the interests exhibited by these students and their professional purposes, but the training Shippen gained over a period of two years by the use of his hands in anatomical dissections, injections, and operations on the cadaver and in handling for himself certain obstetrical patients made him an assured practitioner of his specialties when he graduated, while the other three, all trained as internists with heads full of lectures and text book information, were behind him in actual practical experience of dealing personally with patients and the problems of their diseases.

In following the educational program he selected, Shippen was not guided solely by inclination. His medical advisers in London were advocating this very plan of medical training. Examination of an interchange of correspondence between London and New York in 1762 by Samuel Bard, who was enrolled at St. Thomas's Hospital, and his father, Dr. John Bard, who was practicing at home, reveals the fact that both Dr. Fothergill and Colin Mac-Kenzie had advised young Bard to adopt a plan resembling Shippen's by spending a winter in London, following his summer in the hospitals, before removal to Edinburgh. Their reasons were that they thought it best to " lay a foundation in practice [before entering] upon theory." This advice conflicted with Dr. John Bard's who advocated immediate connection with the University of Edinburgh, and Samuel Bard left London late that summer.[15] Unfortunately for him he had not been exposed to the influence of William Hunter's school of anatomy. Dr. Hunter's courses in anatomy had been temporarily suspended during the spring of his arrival as well as during the previous autumn. John Hunter had gone to Belleisle as surgeon in the British Army, and Dr. Hunter himself, immersed in a steadily increasing private practice, was especially concerned with the care of Queen Charlotte " as a child-bearing Lady " with expectations.[16] Lack of opportunity to work with the Hunters may be regarded as a strong factor in Bard's final decision to proceed to Scotland for continuation of his medical training. In October, 1762, to be sure, Dr. Hunter resumed instruction in anatomy in rooms which he obtained " at the Chelsea China Warehouse in Picadilly near the head of the Haymarket," [17] but by that time Bard was well established in lodgings in Edinburgh. He got settled a month before the term began in order to grow familiar with the Scottish pronunciation of Latin.[18] At the University of Edinburgh his scholarly tastes soon found occupation in botany and belles lettres as well as medicine, and he distinguished himself. After graduation in 1765 he returned at last to London and spent ten months in the hospitals following medical practice instead of surgery,[19] but he seems always to have regretted missing a chance to dissect with the famous Hunters. In Scotland he had been able to secure only " a scull and some old bones " while Monro was lecturing.[20] " To have had a subject in my possession [there, I] would [have] run the risk of banishment if not of life." [21]

Scotland still regarded dissection with strong public disfavor and legal restrictions made it impossible to obtain subjects openly, a situation which fostered the rise of resurrectionists and led to grave disorders in the nineteenth century. Scotland's anatomists always looked upon the Hunterian laboratories as a fountain-head of investigative opportunity and never forgot that the Hunters had been born in Scotland.

[15] MacVickar, 20-27.
[16] Peachey, 113, 114.
[17] *Ibid.*, 118.
[18] MacVickar, 25.

[19] *Ibid.*, 78-81.
[20] *Ibid.*, 35.
[21] *Ibid.*, 44.

In Edinburgh Samuel Bard had made the acquaintance of young Mr. Morgan of Philadelphia. In September, 1762, Bard was living in a small room, getting his own breakfast and supper, and taking dinner " at an ordinary with several very agreeable young men, all students, among them a son of Col. Martin of Hempstead and a Mr. Morgan of Philadelphia, a person of distinguished merit who knew our family, and has taken particular notice of me; and as I can with more freedom apply to him, in any trivial matter, than to a professor, I promise myself much advantage from his friendship." [22]

Late in December, in a revealing letter [23] to his father, an item of medical news from Philadelphia was relayed in roundabout fashion from Edinburgh to New York by Samuel Bard.

Edinburgh, Dec. 29, 1762.

Honoured Sir,

You no doubt have heard that Dr. Shippen has opened an anatomical class in Philadelphia; his character here as an anatomist is very good and no doubt he appears equally so in America. You perhaps are not acquainted with the whole of that scheme; it is not to stop with anatomy but to found, under the patronage of Dr. Fothergill, a medical school in that place: Mr. Morgan who is to graduate next spring and will be over in the fall, intends to lecture upon the theory and practice of physic and is equal to the undertaking. I wish with all my heart they were at New York that I might have a share amongst them and assist in founding the first medical college in America. I do not want ambition to prompt me to an undertaking of this kind and I have had some conversation with my friend, Mr. Martin respecting it, but I am afraid that the Philadelphians, who will have the start of us by several years will be a great obstacle. . . . I own I feel a little jealous of the Philadelphians, and should be glad to see the College of New York at least upon an equality with theirs.

Your affectionate son,

S. B.

[22] *Ibid.*, 33, 34.
[23] *Ibid.*, 37, 38.

Marriage in London; Anatomy and Obstetrics in Philadelphia

AFTER four years of absence in the British Isles William Shippen, Jr. arrived in Philadelphia with an Edinburgh medical degree and a wife. He had met Alice Lee of Virginia in England, expatriated by her own wish, and living in London with her cousins the Ludwells.[1] She had six brothers, she told him; two younger ones, Arthur and William, were also in England for their education. Arthur, four years Shippen's junior, after finishing at Eton had elected to study medicine, would graduate from Edinburgh in 1764—and later, taking up the study of law, would become involved with international politics. As young Americans together in a foreign land, Alice Lee, "expressing upon all her features that heavenly mildness which is the characteristick of her Soul,"[2] and William Shippen, found many interests in common and after Shippen's springtime return to England from a brief fling on the continent in the winter of 1762, they were married in London, April 3, in the Church of St. Mary le Strand, Middlesex. This alliance with the Lees of Virginia, Shippen thought, would be up to the standards set by his father and Uncle Edward of Lancaster. Oddly enough, Alice Lee's dearest English friend, Dr. Robert Home's daughter Anne,[3] would marry, years later in 1771, Mr. John Hunter, the celebrated anatomist who had been the inspiration of William Shippen's student days in London.

[1] Nancy Shippen, *Her journal book*, 53.
[2] *Ibid.*, 84. This description of Alice Lee Shippen is from the pen of Louis Otto, Nancy's suitor. For Shippen's visit to France, see p. 125 n.
[3] *Ibid.*, 52. But Mr. John Hunter was never knighted as Nancy's editor believes in announcing that Anne Home became the wife of Sir John Hunter! He was a *surgeon*, known only as *Mr.* Hunter, in contradistinction to his brother William who, belonging to the Royal College of *Physicians*, was entitled to be called *Doctor* by English usage.

Upon return from his studies abroad Shippen found Philadelphia the same well-built town of straight streets and red brick houses set among shade trees and flowers which he remembered in contrast to London's intricate maze. After his student lodgings in the British Isles how luxurious it was to settle down in Fourth Street in the spacious beautiful rooms of Shippen House [4] where his father lived in great comfort! There were many ties with family and friends to renew. Across the street " Aunt Willing " and her husband were taking pleasure in the development of their acreage into a proper setting for the mansions which his cousins, the Powels, the Byrds, and the Binghams would come to occupy and beautify with gardens.[5] Cousin Edward Shippen lived in Fourth Street, near by, and had a new baby daughter, Peggy, who they little dreamed was destined to take a difficult part in history.[6] Young William Shippen's friends were advancing variously in business; his father welcomed him as a colleague in medicine.

Medical conversations flourished in his father's household. When he asked about the Pennsylvania Hospital, his father told him what a struggle the institution was having to maintain itself financially. Its usefulness was only gradually arousing sufficient public interest. Mr. Franklin's prolonged absence in England was seriously hampering the young institution in its growth. His " influence and prestige " . . . " his experience and energy were

---

[4] *Ibid.*, 15. Shippen House, located at Locust (then Prune) and South Fourth Streets.

[5] *Ibid.*, pp. 54 *n.*, 55 *n.* " Aunt Willing " was Anne Shippen, sister of the elder Dr. William Shippen, and the wife of Charles Willing, the founder of one of the most important families in the colonies. Their daughter Mary married Colonel William Byrd of Westover, Virginia; their daughter Elizabeth married Samuel Powel, prominent Philadelphian; and their son Thomas, first president of the Bank of the U. S., was also president of the provincial Congress and a partner of Robert Morris in the financing of the country during the Revolution. He became the father of Philadelphia's beauty Anne Willing who married William Bingham and was admired in all the courts of Europe (R. W. Griswold, *The Republican court, or American society in the days of Washington*, N. Y., 1854). The Byrd, Powel, and Bingham houses in a garden setting were the " show places " of the colonial city.

[6] Edward Shippen, Jr., 1729-1806, son of Edward of Lancaster, became Chief Justice of Pennsylvania in 1790. His home was at 98 South Fourth Street, later to become the residence of Benjamin Rush. Peggy Shippen, daughter of Edward Shippen, Jr. and Margaret (Francis) Shippen, married Benedict Arnold April 18, 1779 (Nancy Shippen, *Her journal book*, 54; DAB).

no longer available in behalf of the Hospital's interests . . . to press measures to a successful issue " in the Assembly.[7] The Hospital needed especially the energetic support of every physician in the city. Young Shippen knew well from personal experience in England and Scotland the importance of a hospital for the study of disease. Medical education must center about a hospital.

Young Dr. Shippen " lately arrived from London " met the Managers and Treasurer of the Pennsylvania Hospital " in the Warden's Room at the Court House in Philadelphia " on November 8, 1762.[8] He had come to the meeting to inform these gentlement that " Per the Carolina, Capt. Friend, are arrived from Dr. John Fothergill of London Seven Cases which contain a parcel of Anatomical Drawings which the Doctor informed him when in London he intended as a present to the Pennsylvania Hospital." Dr. Fothergill had already written to James Pemberton in July that since " the knowledge of Anatomy is of exceeding great use to Practitioners in Physick and Surgery and [that] the means of procuring Subjects with you are not easy " he would send the Hospital by Dr. Shippen " a present of some intrinsick value " in the form of " some pretty accurate Anatomical Drawings about half as large as the Life [which] have fallen into my hands."

Fothergill's letter to Pemberton had continued with an important proposition for consideration which Shippen now read to them again.

> In the want of real subjects these [drawings and casts] will have their Use & I have recommended it to Dr. Shippen to give a Course of Anatomical Lectures to such as may attend, he is very well qualified for the subject & will soon be followed by an able Assistant Dr. Morgan both of whom I apprehend will not only be useful to the Province in their Employments but if suitably countenanced by the Legislature will be able to erect a School for Physick amongst

---

[7] Morton's *History of the Pennsylvania Hospital* details the early financial struggles of the institution (pp. 46 ff.). The corner-stone of the hospital was laid in May 1755 (Benjamin Franklin wrote the inscription), the roof was raised the October following, and the Managers made an inspection December 27 of the same year (pp. 39, 40), but it was another year before the building was ready for occupancy (Packard, 1: 205). In the meantime James Kinsey's house on Market Street was fitted up and used as a temporary hospital (Morton, 32, 33).

[8] *Ibid.*, 356-357.

you that may draw many students from various parts of America &
the West Indies & at least furnish them with a better Idea of the
Rudiments of their Profession than they have at present on your Side
of the Water.

The Managers had no comment to make on the desirability of
" a School for Physick " in Philadelphia but Shippen's immediate
proposal to use the new collection to illustrate lectures on anatomy
during the coming winter was approved by the physicians present,
and it was voted that the cases from England should be conveyed
to the Hospital for examination.

On the next day, November 9, the Managers and physicians
met again at the Hospital where the seven cases sent by Dr. Fothergill were unpacked and viewed. The minutes read:

> Open'd three cases containing Eighteen different curious Views of
> various parts of the Human Body in Crayons framed and glaized;
> three Cases of Anatomical Castings & one Case containing a Skeleton
> & Foetus.
>
> It is agreed that the preparations should be deposited in the North
> Room on the Second Floor & the same Committee with Samuel
> Rhoads are desired to employ Workmen to affix a Partition in that
> Room & make it convenient for the Purpose.
>
> In order to comply as near as possible with the Intention of the
> Donor it is unanimously agreed that the anatomical Drawings and
> Casts should not be permitted to be taken out of the Room, the
> Key of which is to be put under the particular care of the Managers
> in attendance.
>
> And if any Professor of Anatomy is desirous to exhibit Lectures
> he is to apply to them for Liberty.
>
> All such pupils as attend the said Lectures intended to be exhibited
> by Dr. Shippen or any other person should pay a pistole each.
>
> And such persons who from curiosity may apply to view the said
> Paintings &c. should pay a Dollar each.

No one viewing Dr. Fothergill's gift could appreciate with as
much fervor as young William Shippen this skeleton and foetus,
these drawings and casts. He would put them into service in his
anatomical lectures which Dr. Fothergill had suggested to the
Board and which the Managers were " countenancing in his undertaking." The " set of Anatomical Paintings & Castings in plaister
of Paris representing different views of Several parts of the Human
body " were deposited " in a Convenient Chamber of the Hos-

pital " in accordance with Dr. Fothergill's warning that they
" should not be kept in too dry a place nor shaked about too
much." The entire collection valued then at £350 can still be seen
today on display at the Pennsylvania Hospital. The drawings,
eighteen in number, are the work of the distinguished medical
artist, van Rymsdyk, " drawn from nature by his accurate and
exquisite pencil against a sky-blue background." Some of them
display the gravid uterus in different stages as well as breech and
arm presentations and the foetal circulation, as then understood.
It is possible that these crayon drawings may have been preliminary
studies or discards of illustrations van Rymsdyk was already in
process of producing for William Hunter's great folio, thirty
years in the making, *The Anatomy of the Gravid Uterus*, which
finally appeared in 1774.[9]

In the excitement over this present from Dr. Fothergill, his
earlier suggestion as to the establishment of a " School for
Physick " had been passed over, perhaps with design from a feeling on the part of the hospital authorities that the University was
as yet too feeble financially to carry so elaborate an enterprise.
The Shippens, undiscouraged, began at once to put into operation
plans for opening a private school of anatomy like the Hunters.
There was room on the grounds of Shippen House to build unpre-
tentious quarters or adapt a carriage house, perhaps, on the Prune
Street side, and ten young gentlemen were soon gathering there
for anatomical lectures.

Shippen advertised his lectures in the *Pennsylvania Gazette* as
early as November 11 " for the advantage of young gentlemen
now engaged in the study of physick in this and the neighboring
provinces whose circumstances and connections will not admit of
their going abroad for improvement to the anatomical schools in
Europe." Shippen would " demonstrate the situation, figure and
structure of all parts of the Human body," explain " their respec-

[9] Dr. Francis R. Packard has reproduced these " Fothergill pictures " in his
chapter on *Education before the medical schools* (Packard, 1, chap. V: 273-337).
The pictures were first used in reproduction by E. B. Krumbhaar, History of
anatomy in the United States, *Annals of Med. Hist.*, 4(3), 1922. Jan van
Rymsdyk, the artist who illustrated William Hunter's great work *The gravid uterus*,
was a native of Holland. His son became his assistant. R. Hingston Fox (*op. cit.*)
credits these eighteen drawings to van Rymsdyk, Sr.

Fig. 7. William Hunter lecturing on anatomy to the Royal Academy.

Fig. 8. The Pennsylvania Hospital.

tive uses and as far as a course in anatomy will permit their diseases with the indications and methods of care briefly treated of." In surgery " all the necessary operations will be performed on cadavers, a course of bandages exhibited, and the whole conclude with an explanation of some of the curious phenomena that arise from an examination of the gravid uterus and a few plain directions in the study and practice of midwifery."

Tickets for the course were five pistoles each. " Gentlemen who incline to see the subject prepared for the lectures and to learn the art of dissecting, injecting etc. are to pay five pistoles additional." To gentlemen " who may have the curiosity to understand the anatomy of the Human body " the lectures were also open for their " entertainment " at the price of five pistoles.

An Introductory Lecture to this course (apparently never printed) was ceremoniously delivered by Dr. William Shippen, Jr. at the State House on November 16, at six o'clock in the evening, preliminary to the beginning of instruction on November 26 in Fourth Street. Activity filled his life at the start of his career as a teacher.

In the Pennsylvania Hospital minutes the name of Dr. William Shippen, Jr. next appears on May 17, 1763 when he met the Managers at the London Coffee House and " proposed that an advantage may arise to the Hospital by the Anatomical Drawings and Casts, and offered his services to attend twice in a Month to give some explanation to such persons who may be desirous to see them." A fee of a dollar each " for the benefit of the Hospital " was suggested as a proper charge. This use of the collection for general educational purposes was exactly in accordance with Dr. Fothergill's intention, and the Managers were pleased to comply with Shippen's suggestion.[10] By December, seven months later, the Managers wrote their thanks for the collection rather tardily to their " esteemed patron, Dr. Fothergill, now greatly assisting Franklin and David Barclay in advancing their pecuniary interests in England." With regard to the use of his gift and their future plans, they reported:

[10] Morton, 357, 358.

> The Premium paid for this Privilege [viewing the Collection] hath produced more than we expected and when such Gentlemen of the Faculty who are duly qualified and incited by a desire of promoting public Good will devote their Time and Attention we may hope there will be such Compleat Courses of Lectures given in the various Branches of Physical Knowledge as to render their Service very extensive which it will afford us much Satisfaction and Pleasure to promote.

Medical education in simple form had already started at the Hospital soon after its opening. Attending physicians had brought with them their office students or apprentices to follow the practice of the house and act as dressers, according to the British custom. Such young men were charged fees for the lectures and demonstrations they attended, and the money so obtained was applied to the purchase of medicines and to form a library fund. Special apprentices were in time taken into the Hospital to live. An actual indenture was drawn up, binding the medical apprentice to serve the hospital for five years in return for instruction through service. At the close of this period the successful apprentice received for his performance " a suit of cloathes " and " an engrossed certificate." [11] Among the young men soon to frequent the Hospital was one named Benjamin Rush who went also to Shippen's early anatomical lectures. Rush was not a hospital apprentice but was serving his time " in Dr. Redman's shop," came to the hospital with him, and was admitted to see the practice of five other physicians, he relates in his *Autobiography*.

While the hospital managers and " Gentlemen of the Faculty duly qualified " were taking their time about arrangements for " Compleat Courses in Physical Knowledge," the teaching of anatomy in Fourth Street was progressing, though not without difficulty and opposition. The building where human dissections were made was to be under siege at times, stormed with stones and its windows broken. Once in his career as anatomist Shippen barely escaped injury by running through an alley while the carriage waiting at his door " supposed to contain him received along with a shower of other missiles a musket ball through the center of it." [12] He was forced by such circumstances to write an

[11] *Ibid.*, 479-481.

[12] Some of these events were of later occurrence; one was actuated by a sailors' mob (DAB., Scharf and Westcott, *History of Philadelphia*, 2: 1587, Phila., 1884).

explanation of his purposes and conduct of work to the newspapers for the assurance of people in general that the reports of his raids on cemeteries were absolutely false and that the subjects he dissected were either suicides or criminals, with now and then one from the Potter's Field. Gradually the city got used to the situation and the newspapers stated openly that bodies of suicides and executed prisoners were being sent to Dr. William Shippen, Jr. " for anatomic purposes."

It was not until January 1765 that William Shippen, the anatomist, felt his position secure enough in his first-chosen controversial field to venture to combat the widespread popular prejudice against the man-midwife. Again using the *Pennsylvania Gazette* as his medium he offered in his advertisement of January 31 a complete course in midwifery open to both sexes.[18] Hitherto it had been considered improper if not indecent for a woman in labor to have a male attendant. Dr. Shippen, Jr., took pains to explain his position carefully in this delicate matter. Preceding the advertisement of his course he made a clear statement of his observations as a practitioner of midwifery in exposure of the deplorable situation which he found had arisen through ignorance.

> Dr. Shippen, Jr., having been lately called to the assistance of a number of women in the country, in difficult labours, most of which was made so by the unskillful old women about them, the poor women having suffered extremely, and their innocent little ones being entirely destroyed, whose lives might have been easily saved by proper management, and being informed of several desperate cases in the different neighborhoods which had proved fatal to the mothers as to the infants and were attended with the most painful circumstances too dismal to be related, he thought it his duty immediately to begin his intended courses in Midwifery, and has prepared a proper apparatus for that purpose, in order to instruct those women who have virtue enough to own their ignorance and apply for instructions, as well as those young gentlemen now engaged in the study of that useful and necessary branch of surgery who are taking pains to qualify themselves to practice in different parts of the country with safety and advantage to their fellow citizens.

[18] The advertisement of Shippen's midwifery lectures first appears in the *Pennsylvania Gazette* of January 31, 1765. The usual statement that this advertisement appeared January 1 must be the result of a typographical error made long ago. The *Pennsylvania Gazette* was a weekly, and in 1765 it was issued January 3, 10, 17, 24, 31. There was no issue of this paper on January 1, 1765.

Following this statement came the announcement of the course:

Doctor Shippen, Junior

Proposes to begin his first course on Midwifery as soon as a number of pupils sufficient to defray the necessary expense shall apply. A course will consist of about twenty lectures in which he will treat of that part of anatomy which is necessary to understand that branch—explain all cases of Midwifery—natural, difficult and preternatural—and give directions how to treat them with safety to the mother and child; describe the diseases incident to women and children in the month, and direct to proper remedies; will take occasion during the course to explain and apply those curious anatomical plates and casts of the gravid uterus at the Hospital and conclude the whole with necessary cautions against the dangerous and cruel use of instruments.

In order to make this course more perfect, a convenient lodging is provided for the accommodation of a few poor women who otherwise might suffer for want of the common necessities on those occasions, to be under the care of a sober, honest matron, well acquainted with lying-in women, employed by the Doctor for that purpose. Each pupil to attend two courses at least for which he is to pay five guineas. Perpetual pupils to pay ten guineas. The Doctor may be spoke with at his house in Front Street every morning between the hours of six and nine, or at his office in Laetitia Court every evening.

Students enrolling in the course on midwifery followed a comprehensive set of lectures which developed the subject systematically.

1st. On the Bones of the Pelvis. 2nd. Male and Female Organs. 3rd. Changes in the Uterus. 4th. On the Placenta. 5th and 6th. On the Circulation and Nutrition of the Foetus. 7th. On the Signs of Pregnancy. 8th. On the Menses. 9th. Fluor Albus. 10th. On Natural Labours. 11th. and succeeding ones on Labourious and Preternatural Labours, with the use of Instruments; and concluded by particular lectures on the Diseases of Women and Children within the month and directions concerning the diet of each, and methods of choosing and making good nurses.[14]

In his Introductory Lecture to this course Shippen outlined his general procedure. At his " lodging for the accommodation of a few poor lying-in women," presumably in Laetitia Court, near

---

[14] Quotations from George W. Norris, *The early history of medicine in Philadelphia*, 43 ff., Phila., 1886.

the water front, he hoped that each of his students might handle at least one natural labour. He would demonstrate to them all kinds of difficult and " preternatural " labours with the machine he had provided. Again he emphasized that he would give every necessary direction to enable them " to manage all cases with the greatest safety to mother and child." In conclusion he presented a résumé of the history of midwifery in which he had opportunity to pay tribute to his masters, Colin Mackenzie and William Hunter, and to recommend the observation of their principle, and his own, of " *grave deportment* to gain the good opinion of the female world." He particularly deplored a jocular attitude about the patient or the profession of midwifery. He warned against the danger of acquiring the habit of alcoholism which " insensibly by taking a dram in a cold or wet morning " might become overpowering. His attitude toward fees was " Charge no one extravagantly, and every one in proportion to their abilities, remembering that by giving your service gratuitously to the poor you will get much from the rich." This last admonition to his hearers perhaps echoes a conversation in London with Dr. Fothergill who is credited as the first to have made the often repeated remark that to acquire experience and a good living in the practice of medicine one should creep over the backs of the poor to dip into the pockets of the rich.[15] London's voice could always be heard in Shippen's every medical word and professional act.

[15] MacVickar, 81.

America's First Medical School;
Association of Shippen, Morgan,
and Rush

EDINBURGH was to speak especially through John Morgan of
Philadelphia for academic medical teaching. John Morgan
with his organizational genius was to push through to accomplishment the founding of a medical school in Philadelphia, an enterprise which had been germinating for several years in many minds.
Morgan arrived in Philadelphia from his European travels in the
spring of 1765 soon after Shippen's obstetrical course had begun.
Following graduation in Edinburgh, Morgan had been in England again; he had spent a winter in Paris, the peace treaty having
been signed in 1763, studying anatomy with Sue; and in Italy he
had enjoyed the society of the venerable Morgagni who had
claimed him as a kinsman and gained his admission to the Society
of Belles Lettres in Rome. Morgan returned to Philadelphia
with the right to a glittering string of letters after his name. He
had achieved election to the Royal Society in England through the
excellence of his investigations and his injections; he had also
become corresponding member of the Académie Royale de Chi-
rurgie de Paris, licentiate of the Royal College of Physicians of
London, and member of the Royal College of Physicians in Edinburgh.[1] Good looking, fluent, able, the Trustees of the College
of Philadelphia found him impressive. Already there had been
presented to them under date of February 15, 1765, a letter from
Thomas Penn, the Proprietor, recommending " the introduction
of new professorships into the College for all such as shall incline
to go into the study and practice of Physick and Surgery, as well

[1] See James Thomas Flexner's glowing account of John Morgan in *Doctors on
horseback*, 3-53, N. Y., Viking, 1937.

106

as the several Occupations attending upon these necessary and useful Arts." [2]

Dr. Thomas Bond and his brother, Dr. Phineas Bond, Dr. Cadwalader, and Dr. Redman, Morgan's former preceptor, made up a medical group among the trustees who listened with extraordinary interest to this communication, with its warm commendation of the bearer, and to another letter advocating the scheme which was signed by two trustees absent at this time in England, the Honorable James Hamilton, Esq., well known to them through previous administrations as their lieutenant governor, and the Reverend Richard Peters, pastor of Philadelphia's United Churches of Christ and St. Peter's. When Penn's proposition was put to vote, the Board of Trustees was unanimous in its support. Furthermore

> The above Letters and Proposals being duly weighed and the Trustees entertaining a high sense of Mr. Morgan's abilities and the Honours paid to him by different Bodies and Societies in Europe, they unanimously appointed him Professor of the Theory and Practice of Physick in the College.

The well planned campaign was won. Philadelphia would have the first medical school in America and John Morgan had been appointed to the first medical professorship.[3] Four weeks later at the Commencement of the College of Philadelphia John Morgan, twenty-nine, delivered his epoch-making *Discourse Upon the Institution of Medical Schools in America*, said to have been prepared by him in Paris. Commencement Exercises took place in the Academy building on Fourth Street near Arch, originally erected for George Whitefield's preaching. May 30, Commencement Day, "being very warm" only half of the discourse was delivered that day. The meeting was adjourned to "Friday Forenoon, May 31" for "the remainder of his learned and elaborate oration," [4] soon to be issued from the press of William Bradford.

Morgan sketched his qualifications without embarrassment, claiming more than fifteen years of preparation in medicine,

---

[2] Montgomery, 479.

[3] *Ibid.*, 480.

[4] *Ibid.*, 453, 454 (Dr. William Smith's minutes reporting proceedings of Commencement).

beginning with early apprenticeship to Dr. John Redman, con-
tinuing during four years of military life and concluding with
five years of study in Europe " under celebrated masters in every
branch of medicine " sparing " no labor or expense " to store his
mind " with an extensive acquaintance in every science that related in any way to the duty of a physician." [5]   There was to be
" nothing narrow or meagre " in this first medical college in the
new world; it should be an example to the whole country, a continent offering " the greatest mines of knowledge yet unrifled."
The purpose was approved by " the great and well known Dr.
Fothergill, the justly celebrated Dr. Hunter " and others.   The
time had come to establish in this new land a distinction between
the different orders of physicians, surgeons, and apothecaries.
Each man should have his own field of work.   Difficulties they
must regard as left by others for them to master.   He took satisfaction in recommending Dr. Shippen to the Trustees as worthy
of a professorship of anatomy.   He understood that Dr. Shippen
in a lecture introductory to his first anatomical course had proposed some *hints* of a plan for giving medical lectures.   " I do not
learn," said Morgan, " that he recommended at all a collegiate
undertaking of this kind. . . .   Dr. Shippen having been concerned
already in teaching anatomy is a circumstance favourable to our
wishes."   Few could be " ignorant of the great opportunities he
has had abroad of qualifying himself in anatomy and that he
already has given three courses thereof and designs to enter upon
a fourth course. . . ."   Morgan appealed " to the common sense of
mankind " for the furtherance of his plans.   Edinburgh was evidently to be the model for the new institution where medicine
should be taught " in its fullness founded deep upon kindred
sciences."

To physicians in his audience Morgan's discourse was highly
provocative.   His views, the commonplace of today's medical practice, were far in advance of those held by most of his American

---

[5] A copy of Morgan's *Discourse* has been examined at the Historical Society of
Philadelphia.   By Morgan's claim he must have begun his medical preparation at
fourteen, presumably as office boy.   While writing his *Discourse* in Paris he speaks
of himself as middle-aged at twenty-eight.   Ironically enough, Morgan died in his
fifty-fourth year.

contemporaries.   Candidates for the new school must fulfill requirements of a high order.   Their pre-medical studies must have included mathematics, natural science, Latin, and if possible a modern language.   As apprentices they must have acquired a knowledge of pharmacy and the rudiments of medicine.   In the medical school they would begin with anatomy and proceed to lectures in materia medica, botany, chemistry, and clinical medicine.   Following theory, a year of work in the Pennsylvania Hospital would make a student eligible for the degree of Bachelor of Medicine.   To become a Doctor of Medicine he must practice three years and then return to write a thesis contributing to medical knowledge.   Morgan felt that the apprentice system was not only antiquated but dangerous without a background of sound learning.   He was equally against the doctor who combined the functions of physician, surgeon, apothecary, and dentist.   Nobody could be equally skilled in half a dozen pursuits.   The doctor must select a specialty and stick to it.   His was physic.   He should send his surgical cases to a man who specialized in surgery.   He would not even compound his own medicines.   He had brought from England an apothecary, Mr. David Leighton, " with a large stock of drugs prepared by Silvanus and Timothy Bevan," of high repute as pharmacists, and he recommended the services of this apothecary to all physicians present.   His medical listeners, somewhat bewildered by the fury of his enthusiasm, felt that he was an iconoclast, breaking to pieces the traditional structure of medical practice which they had devoted their lives to building.

William Shippen, Jr., seems to have kept silent in spite of what he considered Morgan's misrepresentation until a letter of his composition was read at a Trustee's meeting on September 23.   It was ostensibly a letter of application for a professorship of anatomy and surgery in the new school, but the writer took pains to make plain in a dignified statement the background of Morgan's proposition.[6]

Philadelphia, September 17, 1765.

To the Trustees of the College

The instituting of medical schools in this country has been a favorite object of my attention for seven years past, and it is three

[6] Packard, 1: 348; Montgomery, 481.

years since I proposed the expediency and practicability of teaching medicine in all its branches in this city, in a public oration, read at the State House, introductory to my first course of Anatomy.

I should have long since sought the patronage of the Trustees of this College, but waited to be joined by Dr. Morgan, to whom I first communicated my plan in England, and who promised to unite with me in every scheme we might think necessary for the execution of so important a point. I am pleased, however, to hear that you gentlemen on being applied to by Dr. Morgan, have taken the plan under your protection, and have appointed that gentleman Professor of Medicine.

A professorship of Anatomy and Surgery will be gratefully accepted by, gentlemen, your most obedient and humble servant,

William Shippen, Jr.

Shippen, perfectly fitted for the position, immediately received appointment in September, 1765, as professor of anatomy and surgery in the new medical school of the College of Philadelphia, the second appointment made by the Trustees to its faculty. His classes were the first to be organized for instruction. Shippen gave his first lecture in anatomy November 14, 1765. Morgan's course in the theory and practice of physic took shape in lectures delivered during that winter [7] and expanded for the session beginning September 25, 1766.

The new school of medicine held its first Commencement on June 21, 1768.[8] There were eight graduates, John Archer of New Castle county being alphabetically the first. Provost William Smith saw to it that Dr. Shippen, Jr., had an important part in the exercises by giving the final charge to the students he had first taught. Two other young men were soon to augment the faculty. Adam Kuhn, trained by Linnaeus at Upsala as botanist and by Hope at Edinburgh in materia medica, was elected professor of those specialties in 1768, and the next year Benjamin Rush, disciple of William Cullen, was chosen professor of chemistry. Rush

[7] Morgan's lectures actually began only a few days after Shippen's on November 18 according to Packard (p. 352) and were given three times a week. These lectures must have been very elementary. " Useful observations on medicine in general " together with " a general idea of chemistry and pharmacy " were promised in the prospectus of the course, the whole to be " illustrated with many useful practical observations on Diseases, Diet and Medicines."

[8] Packard, **1**: 358-360.

was only twenty-four but Dr. Fothergill considered him already " an expert Chymist," Edinburgh held him in high esteem and Penn commended him to the notice of the Trustees. During a career of more than forty years Rush was to distinguish himself as an able practitioner and teacher, a whole-souled patriot, constructive humanitarian, and contributor to Philadelphia's culture. Kuhn was twenty-eight, Shippen thirty-three, and Morgan thirty-four when with young Rush they united the wisdom acquired by superior training with the strength and ambition of their youth to make the new school a power in medical education which should never loose its impetus as the country grew and other medical schools sprang into being. All these young men had been trained by the keen intellects of the Edinburgh faculty,[9] and Shippen had known from his start in London that he must never swerve from specialization in anatomy and its application to the problems of midwifery until he became equally proficient in both subjects.

What has happened meantime to Morgan's friend, Samuel Bard of New York, likewise trained in Edinburgh, who had learned in Scotland what the young Philadelphia physicians were planning? Immediately upon Bard's return from five years of study in the British Isles he had begun his efforts in the city of New York for establishment of a medical school there. Dr. John Bard, his father, had the scheme at heart and had worked in its favor during his son's absence. With the proper influence the New York school had an early start in 1768 as a part of King's College.[10] The jealousy Samuel Bard had confessed years ago in Edinburgh, when rumors of a plan for a medical school in Philadelphia became student gossip in Scotland, completely vanished as his devotion to the new institution he helped to launch in New York, with assistance from an able group of older men as faculty, became the motive power of his life. In his twenty-eighth year Bard had been given by common consent the headship of " the most responsible and influential department of the Practice of Physick " in the medical school at King's College. What did it matter if the New York school could not be the *first* school of

---

[9] *Ibid.*, 361-366. [10] MacVickar, 89-92.

medicine founded in this country? Its sphere of usefulness and influence was assured. Like missionaries of the faith, this Edinburgh band of medical brothers—Bard, Morgan, Rush, and Shippen—would disseminate their true doctrine wherever placed throughout America.

Although Shippen did not possess the abilities of a large-scale organizer he had been successful in his own field in 1762 by instituting a thoroughly developed program of lectures in anatomy, the first systematic medical teaching of academic standard accomplished in the American colonies. In 1765 he had presented the first course in obstetrics ever given in America, its privileges open to both men and women. He had founded that same year a small private lying-in hospital, an innovation in Philadelphia and indeed for the whole country. The Pennsylvania Hospital would not acquire lying-in facilities in a special department until 1803.[11] In the new medical school Shippen's appointment as professor of anatomy gave him the distinction of starting instruction when the first students enrolled for their first lectures in November 1765. This was the beginning of a long career of anatomical teaching in which he was engaged for forty years, with additional teaching in surgery and obstetrics. His excursion into administrative work as Director General (1777-1781) of all the Military Hospitals of the American Armies in the Revolution,[12] for which he was temperamentally unfitted, brought him more headaches than honors. His colleagues of the medical faculty, Morgan and Rush, became his immediate subordinates. The tangling of motives actuating Morgan, Shippen, and Rush in their irritations, which began in the old rivalry between Morgan and Shippen over the founding of the medical school, became more involved through the difficult task of organizing hospitals for sick and wounded soldiers. Rush probably felt that his abilities, unrecognized by Washington, fitted

[11] Plans for the Lying-in Ward were advertised in the *American Daily Advertiser*, February 22, 1803 and it was actually opened May 10, 1803 (Montgomery, 235).

[12] See Packard, 1: chap. VIII, The medical profession in the War for Independence; James Thomas Flexner, *Doctors on horseback* (Sketches of John Morgan and Benjamin Rush), N. Y., Viking, 1937; Nathan G. Goodman, *Benjamin Rush, physician and citizen*, Phila., Univ. of Penn. Press, 1934, for more complete consideration of this undertaking and the rivalries it involved.

him for the undertaking for which both Morgan and Shippen proved unequal.

In 1775 John Morgan, with a ten years' reputation as successful organizer of the medical school behind him, had seemed the logical person to receive appointment as Director General and Chief Physician in the medical department of the American Army. He was faced immediately with a tremendous task of organization. In addition to the important duties of medical supervision for which he was actually fitted, Morgan's new office entailed not only arrangements for camps and the adaptation of already existing quarters for the care of the sick and wounded in private houses, inns, schoolhouses, churches, and religious establishments such as the Cloisters of Ephrata, but the duties of purchasing agent. The problem of distribution of equipment—beds, bedding, medicine, and food—to run these places was almost insurmountable, hampered as he was by scarcity of the necessities for hospital maintenance, by the scattered location of improvised accommodations and by primitive methods of transportation. A most discouraging feature of the situation was the lack of qualified doctors and good nurses.

At this time Benjamin Rush, in his dual capacity as chairman of the medical committee of Congress and physician-general of the Middle Department of the Army was in a strategic position. With his keenly critical mind, he observed abuses which he felt must be rectified, but to his chagrin he found both Congress and Washington absorbed with other problems. At first Rush laid the blame for bad conditions at the hospitals upon the existing system, or rather the lack of system, in the running of the medical department and he devoted his letters, reports, recommendations, and plans to pleading for reorganization of the service after the British plan. The reformer was ignored, but a pamphlet from Rush's ever ready pen, *Directions for Preserving the Health of Soldiers,* first printed in the *Pennsylvania Packet,* was recognized for its merits and published by the Board of War.

At the outset of the Revolution Dr. William Shippen, Jr., as a subordinate of Dr. Morgan, had been assigned to a minor post as director of a small hospital at the Flying Camp in New Jersey.

From this post he was promoted by Congress in the autumn of 1776 to directorship of the hospitals west of the Hudson River. Henceforth he reported directly to Congress without reference to Morgan. That winter he shared with Dr. John Cochran in a plan for reorganization of the military hospital set-up which was sent to Congress for consideration. In the spring of 1777 Congress appointed Dr. Shippen, Jr., as Director General, and Dr. Morgan was withdrawn from the medical service of the Army. John Morgan's removal from office was an act done summarily without express charges, but with evident implication of incompetence and mismanagement. Morgan, completely unprepared for this development, suffered great mental agony but prepared to struggle for congressional vindication. Rush now redoubled his efforts in a fight which went on for many rounds. Rush had changed the emphasis in his complaints. The suffering he had seen among the sick and wounded, the spread of disease within the hospitals, the dearth of supplies and their evident misappropriation when available, the growing lack of regulation in hospital administration incensed him. He felt the need to blame it all upon one person, and Morgan having gone, Shippen as Director General became the scapegoat. The situation growing worse became intolerable to Rush and in 1778 he resigned his medical duties, in spite of his friend, John Adams, who had counseled: "Patience, patience, patience."

Rush's attack upon Shippen culminated in a letter to Washington, actuated by his wish to have Shippen court-martialed. Washington sent Dr. Rush's letter to Congress with its "charges of a very heinous nature against the Director-General, Doctor Shippen, for mal-practices and neglect in his department." The letter, turned over to a congressional committee, was temporarily pigeonholed. In spite of criticism Shippen continued absorbed in his work as Director General, while Rush, nursing resentment in Princeton, seriously considered leaving the medical world and taking up the study of law under the patronage of his father-in-law, Richard Stockton.

The news of the British evacuation of Philadelphia (August, 1778) luckily prevented the realization of this quixotic plan.

Rush returned to private practice in Philadelphia. He found John Morgan a bitter man fighting to clear his reputation as hospital administrator in the Army. In 1777 Morgan had put his grievances into words in a pamphlet entitled *A Vindication of his Public Character in the Station of Director General of the Military Hospitals and Physician-in-Chief to the American Army*, which was published in Boston. Two years dragged by after its publication before official vindication by congressional act was granted him in 1779. Almost immediately Morgan, still smarting from old wounds to his self-esteem, wrote a vindictive letter to Congress charging Shippen with malpractice and misconduct in administration, for which he offered to produce evidence. Shippen countered, as soon as he heard this, by asking Washington to bring the whole matter into clear light by a court-martial. In the events which followed Rush was naturally Morgan's ally.

Shippen was court-martialed March 15, 1780 at Morristown, New Jersey, where proceedings, slow to begin, dragged out at a trial of three months duration, spoiling April, May, and June with its dissensions. Excitement leading to accusations, bitterness, display of personal animosity—all the fruits of jealousy—characterized the testimony day after day, but the evidence after all was legally inconclusive. Since the charges could not be reliably substantiated, Shippen was exonerated. Although in August Congress discharged him from his administrative post, in October the same body of statesmen, having accomplished reorganization of the medical department, reappointed Shippen as Director General, an office which he held for three months only, in token of restoration to public esteem, before returning to resume gradually the duties of practice and of teaching. How Shippen, Morgan, and Rush, working thereafter as fellow faculty members in the medical school, apparently maintained a gentlemen's agreement to live in educational harmony is a puzzle. Morgan had many illnesses, withdrew from society, and finally died in 1789 in his fifty-fourth year.[13] Benjamin Rush succeeded him in the chair of the theory and practice of medicine in the College of Philadelphia.

[13] Rush reports, October 15, 1789 in his Commonplace Book, that called to visit Dr. Morgan he found him dead in a small hovel, lying on a light dirty bed, surrounded with books and papers. Only a washerwoman, one of his tenants, was

Away from the Army, the classroom, the sickbed, William Shippen led another life as a favorite of society, where Dr. Rush admitted his colleague was "always a welcome and agreeable member." Shippen was a favorite with George Washington who sometimes lodged at Shippen House, a center of patriotic activity before the Revolution and again when re-opened after the British occupation of Philadelphia came to an end. John Adams came there and Alexander Hamilton and the great Jefferson, and Mrs. Shippen's unpredictable, brilliant brothers, Arthur and Francis Lightfoot and Richard Henry and William and Thomas. Daughter Nancy's friends and admirers filled the house with gaiety and her father shared in the enjoyment of their dinners and the music and dancing that followed. Bushrod Washington was one of her beaux, but more serious in their attentions were Monsieur Louis Otto, a young French diplomat, and worldly wise Colonel Harry Livingston, a much older suitor. She loved young Otto but it would be more politic "they said" to marry the distinguished officer of the Continental Army, scion of the great house of Livingston, the wealthiest land-owning family in New York state. Dr. Shippen, Jr., always fond of dancing, gave his support to the Philadelphia Dancing Assemblies, the oldest series of subscription balls in America, by serving twenty years on their board of directors. It was a source of pride to him to receive the honor of election to the American Philosophical Society to which both he and his father gained admission in November 1767.[14] Uncle Edward of Lancaster and his sons Edward (who became Chief Justice of Pennsylvania in 1790) and "cousin-colonel" Joseph were also members. In this varied circle Shippen's life was too pleasant to wish

there to care for him but a niece had arrived in time to see him draw his last breath. He died of influenza, apparently. "What a change," Rush concludes, "from his former rank and prospects in Life! The man who once filled half the world with his name had now scarcely friends enough to bury him" (Rush *Autobiography*, ed. Corner, 180).

[14] William Shippen, Jr.'s name appears in the membership list of the American Philosophical Society and also in the list of directors of the Philadelphia Assemblies. Ethel Armes, as editor of Nancy Shippen's *Journal book*, details fully the social life he enjoyed with his family at Shippen House. Dr. William Shippen, Jr.'s son, Thomas Lee Shippen, was elected to the American Philosophical Society in 1793. A young man of great promise he had enjoyed the favor of much personal attention from Thomas Jefferson. For first mention of T.L.S. see p. 3.

for change, or even to feel the urgency for reform of man's oppressive systems which goaded Rush on his sensitive journey through life. Friends sought Dr. Shippen's company eagerly. Members of the Philosophical Society, representatives of the first foreign legations sent to the United States, members of each succeeding Congress thronged to Shippen House to enjoy its well-known hospitality.

To this house, alas, sorrow came, unbidden, in the early death of six [15] of the eight children born to William Shippen and Alice Lee, by the unhappy marriage of their daughter, Nancy, to Colonel Livingston, and the untimely loss, probably from tuberculosis, of their only surviving son, Thomas Lee, at the outset of his career as a lawyer. Dr. Shippen never recovered his buoyancy after this last blow to his hopes, and Mrs. Shippen, having earlier taken to religion as a solace for the woes of her life, became a recluse, joined in time by an equally melancholy daughter. After he gave up practice in 1798 and when his teaching burden became lighter by the help of his devoted pupil, Caspar Wistar, Dr. Shippen was able to retire to Germantown [16] and to engage in quiet pursuits. Turning the pages of his Greek testament, for he still loved the classics in which he had excelled, he would sometimes pause to wander back in thought over the events of a life which had not entirely gratified the ambitions of his youth nor the hopes of his maturity.

Teaching had been his joy, and as a teacher of distinction he was to be remembered by scores of students and even by that detractor of his character, his associate in many ventures and a disappointed rival for Revolutionary favor, Benjamin Rush, who, attending him on his deathbed, went home that very night to list in his Commonplace Book every fault he thought Shippen possessed. Rush had to admit that in spite of Shippen's fondness for the fleshpots, his delight in young convivial company, his disuse of his talents and his dislike of writing, he had attained some rank in his profession. "With the stock of knowledge he acquired

---

[15] See *Chart of the descendants of Dr. William Shippen*, compiled by Charles R. Hildeburn, contained in Nancy Shippen: *Her journal book.*

[16] Roberdeau Buchanan, *Genealogy of the descendants of Dr. William Shippen, the Elder, of Philadelphia*, Washington, 1877.

when young," Rush wrote, " as a teacher of anatomy he was eloquent, pleasing and luminous." Shippen's faults having been carefully enumerated, Rush concluded his summing up sententiously:
Shippen " died a believer in the Gospel. Over his faults let charity
cast a veil. He was my enemy from the time of my settlement in
Philadelphia in 1769 until the day of his death July 11, 1808.
He sent for me to attend him, notwithstanding, in his last illness,
which I did with a sincere desire to prolong his life. Peace and
joy to his soul for ever and ever." [17]

Looking at the highbred face shown in Shippen's portrait in
his maturity one is impressed by the benignity and poise of his
countenance. The eyes with direct gaze are troubled, the mouth
generous, the chin firm. It is the face of a man of character and
personal dignity whom patients can trust.[18]

Elizabeth Drinker's diary of this period is apparently the only
surviving record of Dr. Shippen's practice.[19] Its pages bear wit-
ness to his devotion and skill as a practitioner of obstetrics while
caring for her daughter Sally, often subjected " to the incessant
trial of childbearing." Summoned in April 1795 to attend Sally
in labour, her mother writes, Dr. Shippen found her " difficulties
call'd for his skill more particularly; by good management he
brought on a footling labour which tho' severe has terminated by
divine favour, I trust safely, . . ." Two women, Neighbor Waln
and Hannah Yerkes, probably experienced midwives, had served
in the patient's room while her doctor performed the safe delivery

---

[17] Rush, *Autobiography*, ed. Corner, 322, 323. This was the private conclusion
Rush reached, but to the public he declared in " an eloquent memorial oration ":
" The most ancient and most prominent pillar of our medical school is fallen, and
the founder of anatomical instruction in the United States is no more. Hung be
his theatre in black! And let his numerous pupils in every part of our country
unite with us in dropping a grateful tear to his memory." Quoted by James
Thomas Flexner in his sketch of Benjamin Rush in *Doctors on horseback*, 88, N. Y.,
Viking, 1927.

[18] Painted about 1798 by Gilbert Stuart, a " bust portrait, three quarters to the
right with his gray-blue eyes directed to the spectator. He wears a black coat, white
neckcloth, white lace jabot; his hair is powdered and his complexion ruddy. In
the background is a red curtain " (*Gilbert Stuart, An illustrative descriptive list of
his works*, 2: 688; 3: 726, compiled by Laurence Park, N. Y., Rudge, 1926).

[19] For this account of Dr. Shippen's patients I am indebted to Dr. Cecil K.
Drinker, who has kindly allowed me to make use of material contained in his
book, *Not so long ago*, N. Y., Oxford Univ. Press, 1937.

of the child by version. All three went home next day—" no Nurse as yet obtained to our mind. The little one seems hart whole, tho' the blood is settled in his legs feet &c., his feet almost as blue as indigo. Sally sleeps sweetly this afternoon . . . the child put to the breast this evens."

Sally's sister, Molly, was not as fortunate when attended two years later by a different doctor, a general practitioner who had the reputation of being conscientious but was not a specialist. Dr. Shippen it seems could not be in attendance because he was again needed by Sally whose difficulties as " a child-bearing Lady " he so well understood. Among the Philadelphia doctors of his day, and with a generation still considering the man-midwife doubtfully, Dr. Shippen's success as an obstetrician made him outstanding. Elizabeth Drinker's pages give an account of the prolonged labour which Molly endured at this time under the care of Dr. Nicholas Way. Molly's difficulties were undoubtedly due to uterine inertia, a common obstetrical complication among the women of her family one understands from the diary. Molly's child, another footling presentation produced by version, was stillborn and Molly herself, badly torn, suffered virtual semi-invalidism the rest of her restricted life as the result of a serious rectovaginal fistula, a condition now seldom encountered under modern obstetrical procedure. Her injury may well have resulted from unskilled obstetrical manipulation, or by " a long period of pressure by the presenting part with consequent interference with the blood supply and eventual tearing of devitalized tissues." Although Dr. Shippen as a general rule in obstetrical practice sanctioned operative delivery only for occasional use in extremity, he would probably have considered interference necessary in this case.

He seems to have managed Sally's sixth and last labor with conservative concern successfully. In October 1799 Sally came into labor on her thirty-eighth birthday. Dr. Shippen found her in great distress, restless, " sometimes in bed, sometimes in the Easy Chair as it is called." Early in the morning he bled her " taking 12 or 14 ounces. She had 80 or 90 drops of liquid ladanum during the day and night but not many minuits of sleep for 48 hours— the Dr says the child is wedg'd on or near the shear [pubic] bone and he cannot get to it to alter the position of the head."

Elizabeth Drinker could hardly bear the strain of her daughter's
ordeal. An opium pill of three grains was administered to the
patient after breakfast " to ease her pain or bring it on more
violently, but nothing happened. . . . In the afternoon the Doctor
said the child must be brought forward—he went out . . . that
he was going to bring instruments occurred to me, but I did not
ask him, least he should answer in the affirmative—towards evening I came home as usual . . . when Dan told us that his Mistress
had a fine boy and was as well as could be expected. I was thank-
ful that I happened to be away at the time. Dr. Shippen told me
that he thought he should have occasion for instruments, which,
said he, I have in my pocket, clapping his hand on his side, when I
heard them rattle; but some time after you went away, I found
matters were changed for the better. The Child, said he, is a
very large one for Sally. It is a very fine lusty fatt boy. . . . The
Doctor was very kind and attentive during the whole afflicting
scene, was there two days and two nights and slep't very little."

Phlebotomy, the practice commonly called *bleeding* a patient,
as a method of therapy in uterine inertia, found its justification in
the medical theory of the period as to the importance of plethora,
an unhealthy condition characterized by an excess of blood or of
nutritive substance in the body. Most of the ills of which pregnant
women complained were ascribed by the doctors of that day to
plethora, for which the obvious remedy was bleeding. A plethoric
disposition could be " aggravated by improper or heating food,
by violent exercises or strong liquors freely or imprudently drank."
When the plethoric pregnant patient went into labor it was believed that the stimulus of her exertions would be sufficient " in
a constitution so predisposed, to produce fever, puerperal con-
vulsions, haemorrhages upon the detachment of the placenta,
inflammation of the uterus and peritoneum, inflammation of the
breast and other diseases of similar kind." Plethora's superabund-
ance, it seemed, was the cause of every " female complaint "; was
it not also responsible for abortions? This question, once raised,
" requires most particular attention." Plethora, always suspect,
" especially obtains in the young and vigorous, or in those who live
luxuriously and sleep in soft, warm beds."

As to instrumental deliveries in childbirth which Elizabeth Drinker dreaded in Sally's case, Dr. Shippen in his restrained use of instruments was perpetuating the teaching he had received in London. It is said that William Hunter showed his students his forceps covered with rust from disuse. Instrumental delivery in childbirth had been made popular in England through its successful demonstration (1752-1759) in the practice of William Smellie but when employed by the unskilled it could prove harmful if not disastrous. A sound knowledge of anatomy and good judgment as to the moment of application were requirements for successful use. In modern medical thought forceps deliveries are accepted as a means of prevention of possible harm to both mother and child.[20]

After the child's birth, the eighteenth-century physician took charge of the health of both mother and child since the care and feeding of the child as a separate entity had not yet been undertaken by the profession. William Shippen's first obstetrical course concluded with " particular lectures on the diseases of women and children within the month and directions concerning the diet of each." Whatever the directions may have been in detail, we may be sure that he would recommend breast feeding as the healthy course to follow and the simplest in an age when nobody had the slightest knowledge of what constituted a proper diet for infants and young children. If the mother of a newborn child was physically unable to feed her baby at the breast, one would suppose that wet nurses must have been easier to find at a time when death among young infants was distressingly frequent.

The full strength of Shippen's intellect as a doctor was directed toward the overthrow of crippling taboos in his field of medicine. It was a lifetime effort, requiring incessant watchfulness of the public pulse and forced feeding of propaganda to establish in general thought the necessity for human dissection and the value of the medically-trained man-midwife. It was slow work and not

[20] A twentieth-century opinion of these obstetrical cases has been given verbally to the author by Dr. George W. Corner, Jr. of the obstetrical staff of Johns Hopkins Hospital. The account of plethora is taken from an eighteenth-century author, John Burns, whose book, *Observations on abortions*, 2nd American ed., Springfield, 1809, is quoted from by Dr. Drinker.

as sensationally attractive as the spectacular accomplishment of
Benjamin Rush in psychiatry. Rush, with his deep compassion for
the insane, recognizing the fundamental humanity of the mentally
diseased, their need for humane care and occupation, revolutionized
American psychiatric treatment in so far as physical care is concerned. The work undertaken by William Shippen in anatomy
and obstetrics, with their secrets of life at its end and in its beginning, was equally valuable, not only from the point of view of
medical progress but as an important contribution toward over-
coming the cultural lag of eighteenth-century thought with its
misconceptions and prudery about the human body.

We look without success for any collected written records of
Shippen's accomplishment. Letters and investigations were alike
neglected by him in the quick flow of events, but to pin the label
" indolent " upon this able man, as Rush did in his Commonplace
Book, seems too diagrammatic an analysis of Shippen's tempera-
ment. He was an extrovert, happy in the activities of the moment,
restless, eager for change of employment, uncontemplative. His
life in Philadelphia gave him a full program. He shone with
people. He found his students stimulating. His patients drew
forth his interest and compassion. Pleasures shared with family
and friends, participation in organizations newly formed in a new
country, such as the College of Physicians [21] which he helped
establish, patriotic service during the Revolution claimed what
might have been free time. He was living too eagerly and actively
to project a self-conscious image of himself for future generations
to admire. His talents, moreover, were not those of the investigator who is always asking, Why? Perhaps if the Revolution
had not diverted his energies in maturity for five or six years in
his forties, usually the most productive period in a man's life,
some creative force within him, killed perhaps by disuse, might
have brought forth medical research, but it is idle to speculate on
what might have been, or to ask for a larger contribution from

---

[21] The College of Physicians of Philadelphia held its first stated meeting January
2, 1787 and was incorporated two years later. Shippen, Rush, Morgan, Kuhn,
George Glentworth, Gerardus Clarkson, and John Redman were among its twenty-
four founders (George W. Norris, *The early history of medicine in Philadelphia*,
117, 118, Phila., 1886).

one whose life was dedicated to the establishment and elevation of American medical education.

In 1791 the medical school had become a part of the University of Pennsylvania established by legislative act after a struggle too complex to detail here. After Benjamin Rush accepted the chair of the theory and practice of medicine, upon the death of John Morgan in 1789, there were no major changes in the faculty at this period aside from the appointment of Caspar Wistar in 1792 as adjunct professor of anatomy. As a step toward medical concentration, natural history and botany soon became elective subjects in the curriculum. After 1789 the preliminary degree, Bachelor of Medicine, was abolished.[22] Early advisers in Edinburgh had deprecated the awarding of this degree in the first place, but it had been devised to meet the difficulties of colonial conditions.[23] In action the scheme had proved unworkable. Very few students with this preliminary degree had ever re-entered the College, after three years practice as required, to get the final M. D., only attainable by return to student status for another year of lectures, the writing of a thesis, and the bugbear of further examinations. As a result many superficially trained physicians had been foisted upon the public. William Shippen heartily disapproved of what had happened and he had a chance to air his views in 1790 when the Provost appointed him to give the Commencement address or charge to the students graduating in medicine. His address was a straightforward clear statement of what constituted (at the period) a complete medical education and of the reasons why the advanced degree, M. D., was the only goal for the aspiring medical student to seek. Naturally Shippen emphasized the importance of anatomy in the curriculum as the foundation for all future medical training, with a final statement that " Any medical or surgical Knowledge not built on this basis will be false and insecure and I would earnestly advise that no book on the theory and practice of medicine be ever put into the hands of a medical student till he be well acquainted with

[22] Packard, **1**: 371-373.
[23] A letter of Benjamin Rush written from Edinburgh 1768 to John Morgan (quoted, Packard, **1**: 360) reveals Edinburgh's doubts as to the wisdom of conferring the B. M. degree.

anatomy." From their study of anatomy the students would proceed, he said, to the various lectures offered in their specialties by the careful and ingenious Wistar (then lecturing on pharmacy, chemistry, and physiology), by the sagacious and learned Kuhn (materia medica) and the accurate and sensible Griffitts, by the ingenious Barton (botany)—and having thus laid the best foundations, would finish the superstructure by close attention to the teachings of the able and experienced Rush. This address contained matter of such general interest to all physicians and to all prospective patients that it was immediately printed in *The American Museum*, vol. 8, 1790, preserving for us William Shippen's final utterance on his favorite topic of medical education.[24] His outlook was necessarily restricted by the limitations of eighteenth-century medical thought before the upsurge of scientific discovery, but his basic ideas of a sound foundation and thorough study will never be old-fashioned, and these were once principles to fight for in the training of a physician.

The appointment of Caspar Wistar in 1792 as Adjunct Professor of Anatomy proved a great prop to Shippen. Wistar had been his pupil, was now his assistant and would become his successor. He would also be his eulogist. Shippen's health had been failing and he died in the summer of 1808 from what is described by Benjamin Rush in his *Autobiography* as a wasting disease " introduced by an anthrax." [25] Wistar's tribute to William Shippen, an *Eulogium . . . delivered before the College of Physicians of Philadelphia*, March, 1809, reminded his colleagues that Shippen, whose connection with the school of medicine had been continuous since its start and longer than that of any other member of the faculty, had possessed " the peculiar trait of successfully promoting an object of immense utility to his country and that his steadiness in pursuit thereof entitles him to be ranked as one of the benefactors of mankind." Could it be true, as Wistar thought, that Shippen after an eventful life of many conflicts had " left the world without an enemy? " Ancient jealousies and grudges still rankled, we know, in the thoughts of some of his survivors.

---

[24] This address is given in full in Appendix II, pp. 147-151.

[25] A diagnosis in historical retrospect by GWC suggests that the " anthrax " may have been a carbuncle and the debilitating disease diabetes.

Shippen had plenty of faults but his ideals would outlive him and his generation, embodied in the sound structure of American medical education.

As the years passed many members of his profession would remember Dr. Shippen's last public appearance. In the autumn of 1807 he had been asked appropriately enough to return to the medical school to give the customary introductory lecture to the entering class. It was a most gratifying occasion to him. He had taught anatomy to every medical professor on the faculty, he reflected, and some of his pupils were to be found in almost every state " from the Hudson far beyond the Ohio, and from the shores of Lake Erie to the Gulf of Mexico." The original group of eight students of some forty years ago had been followed by scores of others until the present enrollment reached almost four hundred.[26] He was lecturing in the new medical college building " whose architectural beauties do honor to the genius of Mr. Latrobe." An admirer among his listeners reported [27] that on this occasion the orator's " evergreen eloquence " was " flourishing amid the winter of age." Dr. Shippen had passed his seventy-first birthday. This lecture was his valedictory, as it turned out,

[26] A report of this lecture is contained in the *Eulogium on William Shippen, M. D.*, delivered before the College of Physicians of Philadelphia, March, 1809, by Caspar Wistar, M. D., one of the Censors, and Professor of Anatomy in the University of Pennsylvania, *Phila. Jour. Med. and Phys. Sciences*, 5: 173-188, 1822. It is in this eulogy that the statement is first made that William Shippen had spent a few months in France in 1762 through the influence of Sir John Pringle (p. 176). George III " obtained from the Court of France permission for him to travel " in the party of an heiress, Miss Louisa Poyntz (ordered South because " affected with pulmonary consumption ") as her private physician. Late in March he returned to England with letters from Laurence Sterne to Mrs. Sterne and David Garrick (*Letters of Laurence Sterne*, ed. Lewis Perry Curtis, 158, Oxford, Clarendon Press, 1935). In France Thomas François Dalibard had met Shippen and had taken him to the Royal Gardens to see Buffon. Unfortunately Buffon was absent, having gone to present to the King the eighth volume of his Natural History (Franklin Letters, APS, 1: 66, Dalibard to Franklin, Paris février 1762).

[27] Quotations which follow are from *Extract from an eulogium on William Shippen*, M. D., [accredited to Charles Caldwell, M. D.], delivered in the Medical College of Philadelphia, printed for the publisher, 19 ff., Phila., 1818. Caldwell's description of Shippen in his *Autobiography*, chap. III, Phila., 1855, is quite different in character, but Caldwell was known for his caustic tongue and bitter wit. The story appearing there that Shippen read Dr. Hunter's lecture every year as his opening discourse, grew up very likely because of Shippen's well-known veneration for his early teacher whom he was always quoting.

and he seemed to sense it in his concluding words to the young students starting up the long pathway of a medical career: " With due reverence . . . I might say with the venerable Simeon [of the Biblical story], ' Now lettest Thou thy servant depart in peace since my eyes have seen ' the completion of all my labours for the medical school."

Appendix I

William Shippen Jr.'s Doctoral Thesis

A PRESENTATION copy of William Shippen's thesis *De Placentae cum utero nexu* (Edinburgh imprint, 1761), given by its author to Benjamin Franklin, as noted by the recipient on the title-page, and later bound in a volume of medical dissertations in Franklin's library, is now in the Library of the American Philosophical Society. Its twenty-seven pages record faithful observation of experimental work accomplished in London by the Hunter brothers and Colin Mackenzie and its corroboration by Young and the Monros (*pater et filius*) in Edinburgh. In all this work Shippen seems to have played only a student's part except for one experimental observation of his own which is recorded. As he dedicated his pages in flowing Latin to a group of older professional friends in Philadelphia and especially " to the best of fathers," William Shippen, the Elder, he was no doubt fired with the ambition to establish in his native city in America a center for medical experimentation and practice such as he had discovered to his great advantage in Great Britain.

This doctoral dissertation, leaning heavily upon authority as was the custom of the times, is obviously uncertain and obscure about anatomical details. This was inevitable at a time when there was no well-developed science of microscopic anatomy and before the art of injecting the blood vessels, already far advanced as regards displaying the larger arteries and veins, had been extended by later workers to reveal the finer deep vessels. Shippen and his teachers could not have a clear picture of the actual anatomical pattern of the placenta and its circulation. The conclusion they reached that the blood circulation of the foetus is separate from that of the mother, there being no direct connec-

127

tion between their respective blood vessels in the placenta, is perfectly correct, even though the arguments adduced to support it are only partially valid. The further conclusion, that the foetus receives its nourishment from the mother by "absorption" through the placenta from the maternal blood, is also correct in a superficial way, though here again physiology was not at a stage to define "absorption" nor were eighteenth-century physiologists able to visualize the process or to analyze it in terms of filtration, diffusion and secretion.

The following translation of Shippen's Edinburgh dissertation has been made by Dr. George W. Corner in connection with his own historical studies on the placenta.

An

ANATOMICO-MEDICAL DISSERTATION ON THE CONNECTION OF THE PLACENTA WITH THE UTERUS

which

under the favor of Providence,

by the authority of the Very Reverend Dr. John Gowdie, S. T. P., Prefect of the University of Edinburgh,

and with the consent of the honorable Academic Senate and the authority of the distinguished Faculty of Medicine,

was submitted
for examination by persons of learning

by WILLIAM SHIPPEN OF PENNSYLVANIA
a candidate for the degree of Doctor,

seeking the highest honors and privileges in Medicine conferred by custom and law

on the 16th day of September
at the usual time and place
EDINBURGH,

Hamilton, Balfour and Neill,
Printers to the University
1761

To the Eminent

Thomas Bond
Phineas Bond
Thomas Cadwallader
John Redman
Cadwallader Evans

Skillful physicians of the Pennsylvania Hospital, well known and worthy of emulation for their humane character and their kindness to the poor, whose society he greatly desires and seeks,

and to the best of fathers,

WILLIAM SHIPPEN,

A most expert physician of the same Hospital, to whom for fostering care and the singular liberality with which he has always encouraged the education of his son, the fullest tribute of a grateful heart is rightly due,

WILLIAM SHIPPEN

consecrates these first fruits of his studies

✓ ✓ ✓

ANATOMICO-MEDICAL DISSERTATION *

ON THE CONNECTION OF THE PLACENTA WITH THE UTERUS

Not only various famous authors but also our own professors, the celebrated Monro Senior and his son, have written and published extensively on this subject, and yet no one has devoted himself to it comprehensively, and the detailed descriptions always vary with the investigator. If, therefore, I undertake to gather together and to compare all these discrepant and totally contrary

---

* Superscript numbers appearing in the *Dissertation* indicate Shippen's own references which will be found at the end of Appendix I. All have been verified. The translator has followed modern custom in the spelling of *fetus*, eliminating the diphthong of earlier usage.

views and opinions and the arguments with which they are supported; and if I defend with firm reasons those which best satisfy me and seem most plausible; and if I reject other views which are less consistent and are insufficient to explain all the phenomena, I hope that I shall be approved by the professors of this celebrated institution, if not for talent and skill, at least for diligence and zeal in exposition, and that I shall accomplish the duties which the academic laws require of all who seek the coveted honor and reward of faithful endeavor.

I intend to write about the connection of the placenta with the uterus, showing that there is no anastomosis of their respective vessels. This is the goal to which I first direct myself, but I shall in passing also consider how the fetus is nourished after the placenta becomes attached to the uterus. Meanwhile I think it will not be inappropriate to consider various phenomena of the uterus before conception and during pregnancy, than which the animal economy has nothing more remarkable and nothing more inexplicable. I shall also discuss as briefly as possible when and how the placenta adheres to the uterus and how the ovum grows before its attachment.

I shall say nothing about the amniotic fluid, which according to the views of our celebrated teacher, Monro Senior,[1] contributes little to the nutrition of the fetus, or if it contributes anything this is thought not to be essential. I shall not discuss the position, shape, attachments, or appendages of the virgin uterus. Its length is three inches, its width between one and two inches, and it has a very small triangular cavity on the surface of which appear many openings of fluid-secreting vessels. Toward the fundus these openings are found to be the ends of canals arising from the larger branches of the uterine arteries.

The substance of the uterus is compact, white and cellular, interwoven with a great number of blood vessels and with inconspicuous muscle fibres. In pregnant women, however, these fibres become more conspicuous and are arranged more or less circularly, especially in the fundus where Ruysch describes them. Although many anatomists have denied the existence of these fibres, many others seem to me to agree, on the basis of observations and many recent experiments, that there are fibres of this kind, although their arrangement cannot be perceived because there are so many blood vessels interspersed among them.

The uppermost arterial vessels of the uterus arise from the spermatic arteries, the lower from the hypogastric and some branches even from the hemorrhoidal arteries. Entering the uterus through a fold of the peritoneum, they traverse it, frequently anastomosing with each other, and finally send branches into the uterine cavity. These branches, which are impervious to red blood, transmit milk in the fetus and serum in girls, but when at a certain time of life nature opens the fount of the menses they discharge red blood. This occurs earlier or later in different regions according to the heat or coldness of the climate. In this island the menses usually begin at about the age of 14.

Shortly before this time the vessels of the uterus are distended with blood and there are various disagreeable symptoms, for example severe backache and headache, nausea, pimples, etc., all of which clear up when the menstrual flow begins.

Physiologists are uncertain how nature produces this change, setting up the first menstrual flow and afterwards inducing it again at certain intervals of time. The question is unanswerable at present, and is not relevant to our problem.

The veins of the uterus accompany the arteries and are given the same names as the companion vessels. Some writers believe that the veins of the uterus are larger in proportion to the arteries than elsewhere in the body. No valves are seen in them except a few in the spermatic veins.

Haller[2] and Heister[3] and some other writers have seen and described lymphatic vessels, but no one except Morgagni[4] has seen them in the human uterus. It seems to me that there is no doubt of their existence since they are found in all other parts of the body.

The virgin uterus remains in the same condition until the time of conception, that miracle of nature.

A few days after coitus there is seen in the uterus something enveloped by a porous membrane which afterwards encloses the fetus.[5] This membrane is not attached to the uterus before the end of the third month, at which time all the members of the fetus are plainly discernible. Before that, while the whole con-

ceptus does not exceed the size of a goose egg, no bodily parts
can be distinguished within it.   After the beginning of the fourth
month it grows most remarkably from day to day until it is complete in every part and at the end of the ninth month it is expelled
from the uterus into the light of day.   As the ovum thus grows
and expands, the uterus expands in the same proportion until
from a small structure it has at the time of birth become very
large, and its cavity, which before coitus could scarcely be seen,
now contains not only the fetus and its membranes but also the
placenta and a considerable quantity of fluid.   What is even more
remarkable, although it grows so much, its thickness is not even
diminished.   I cannot agree with Diemerbroeck and some others
that its thickness increases and that some muscular tissue is added
for this purpose.   I think, on the contrary, following the view
of the distinguished Hunter [6] and of Monro Junior [7] that the
uterus thus dilated remains of the same thickness, chiefly because
the uterus which was firm, hard, and compact in the virgin becomes soft and spongy during pregnancy and thus easily receives
a great quantity of blood for the purpose of sustaining the fetus
and because all the vessels now carrying this increased blood flow
are everywhere distended throughout the uterus.

The ovum, including when it first reaches the uterus a still
crude and imperfect embryo, is nourished by fluid supplied by
nature's design and absorbed by the openings of the porous surrounding membrane.   When all the bodily parts have been developed sufficiently to be easily distinguished and the ovum has
grown considerably, that is to say, about the end of the third
month, this membrane which is called chorion adheres to the
dilated vessels of the uterus which are now perhaps filled with
red blood, and becomes the placenta.   As the fetus grows from
day to day the placenta also increases in size.   It becomes round
and is divided into lobules.   Its surface next the uterus is convex
and uneven and is covered by the fleecy and villous membrane
derived from the chorion which has already been mentioned; this
membrane infolds itself between the lobules of the placenta just
as the pia mater enwraps the lobes of the brain.

The placenta consists of a substance *sui generis* which when
broken up is not at all unlike the substance of the liver or the

spleen and like those organs contains innumerable twigs of very minute blood vessels. These vessels, where they terminate on the surface of the above-mentioned membrane are so small and so fine that the thinnest fluids, no matter how forcibly they are injected, merely exude from them as perspiration exudes from the skin. On the contrary the vessels of the uterus which open into its cavity are so widely patent during pregnancy that a goose quill can be inserted into them. No vessels indeed can be found on the internal surface of the uterus so small that they may be said to correspond to the vessels of the placenta.

Anyone who deals with the nutrition of the fetus almost always differs from the last person who wrote about it, but the whole contention can be reduced to these two disputed points:

1. Is the blood propelled by the vital power of the mother through the uterine arteries into placental veins which pass to the fetus, so that there is a reciprocal circulation?

2. Or do the ends of the placental veins merely *absorb* as much of the blood as is necessary for nourishing the fetus?

I shall begin by setting forth the arguments by which the first view is supported and shall then try to refute them and to show how weak and false they are. Having done this I shall as it were open a way toward the goal I have set for myself, and I shall demonstrate that the hypothesis of absorption is not only much more plausible but also agrees with all the observed facts.

Whoever was the first to write on this subject asserted the existence of a continuous passage between mother and fetus and all the other writers of that time followed his authority without question. There was nobody before Julius Caesar Arantius who thought of investigating the subject for himself. This investigator ventured to disagree with all the writers of his own and of the previous century and argued so clearly against the old opinion that a majority of the anatomists accepted the view which had been advanced on the basis of his experiments. Nevertheless, many who flourished in this century, Drake, Cowper, Méry, Heister, Boerhaave, Haller, and last of all the open-minded Noortwyk himself, who has written so extensively and plausibly on the subject, have all again returned to the old doctrine.

As the first argument to prove a reciprocal circulation between mother and fetus they call attention to the great loss of blood which takes place when the placenta of an aborting fetus is separated. This, however, does not seem at all pertinent, for (1) if there really were such an anastomosis there would necessarily be an even greater hemorrhage, because the placenta if bound to the uterus by such continuous vessels could not be so much separated without laceration of the vessels. Actually, however, a minimum of blood is lost, by no means as much as commonly thought. Noortwyk [8] informs us that sometimes an abortion takes place in the fourth month without the loss of more blood than might tinge a pint of urine.

(2) If this anastomosis were general and the vessels of the placenta were necessarily torn from the uterus, abortions would not be as frequent as we are accustomed to see; for indeed a greater force would be required for tearing continuous vessels than for separating an adherent placenta.

(3) Many writers contend that unless these vessels were continuous the fetus could not be drained of all its blood nor killed by an immoderate hemorrhage of the mother. Méry states [9] that a certain pregnant woman fell out of a window at the end of the ninth month and having ruptured blood vessels in the abdomen she immediately died of hemorrhage. When he opened the abdomen and uterus of the dead mother he found the placenta everywhere adherent. When the fetus was dissected he discovered that its veins and arteries were quite empty of blood, although he saw no wound, either external or internal, of the fetus nor any blood in the whole cavity of the uterus. He thinks, therefore, that all the blood of the fetus had escaped through the torn vessels of its mother and since there is no other way by which the blood may pass from the fetus to the mother except through the vessels of the fetus and placenta he considers that a reciprocal circulation between mother and fetus necessarily existed before the accident. In this case, however, it seems to me that Méry was deceived by a false observation, or that something extraordinary had happened, or that he had not accurately inspected the blood vessels in the fetus. Rohault,[10] suspecting that what Méry had observed

should be weighed in the balance again, bled a pregnant bitch to death and when he opened the uterus found that the pups which it contained were not only full of blood but were actually living.

I tried the same experiment on a pregnant bitch and examined the vessels of the pups diligently in the presence of Monro Junior, and we both found that not a drop of blood passed from them to the mother. Méry raised the objection to this experiment that if the pups have died before the uterus is opened their blood vessels will be found to be empty; but the objection cannot be raised in the case of my experiment that I had allowed my pups to die before I opened the uterus and inspected them, for I found all the vessels as full as if the pups had been killed after being born at full term. After death moreover, especially if the body has lain dead for some time, very little blood is left in the arteries. Méry himself admits that the vessels were not all empty, and I suspect that they were as full of blood as usual. Granted that they were altogether empty, the fact does not seem to me to demonstrate as clearly as he would have it that the vessels [of the fetus and the mother] are continuous; and if they do not remain completely full I should consider the opposite interpretation to be more probable, for since the blood vessels of a dying or dead animal, especially the terminal branches, appear to collapse and no longer to receive the blood, it should not seem remarkable that the blood does not pass from the fetus to the mother. In fact an animal which has been bled to death always dies before 1/7 of its blood is drawn, as the experiments made by the acute observer Hales proved beyond doubt.

Méry through his entire life always maintained that the blood flow is reciprocal and pertinaciously defended that teaching. Yet there is no doubt but that the most careful and sincere minds are often deceived by one prejudice or another so that their judgment about many things is different from what plain reason would suggest. In view of all this it is not strange that Méry, deceived by his experiments, drew erroneous conclusions. I hope I may be pardoned, if rejecting his opinions and those of others I have aimed to disclose the naked truth.

(4) Some writers think that after the infant has been born

but while the placenta is still inside the uterus and attached to it, more blood flows from the placenta than can be accounted for by its entire weight, and the mother may thus be drained of blood through the cut umbilical cord. If it were indeed true that the vessels of the mother and the fetus are continuous this would be a great argument. I flatly deny that this has happened, all the more because I have found no one worthy of confidence who affirms it. Daily experience also contradicts it. In fact, umbilical cords are safely cut every day after the birth of the infant but before delivery of the placenta and the cord is rarely tied. No more blood is seen than we believe would easily be contained by the cord itself. An exception is constituted by twin births in which one of the cords sometimes communicates with the other and after the birth of the first infant the second may bleed to death if the cord is not firmly tied. The almost infinite experience of those most distinguished men Hunter, Mackenzie, and our own Young, more proficient than anyone else in this subject, confirms this observation.

It certainly seems to me that a strong argument can be adduced in favor of the contrary view, for if the vital force of the mother drives the blood through the placenta and the fetus, as all the supporters of this teaching declare, I ask why is this force suppressed as soon as the cord is cut? Why does the mother not bleed to death through the cord if it is not tied? Why, moreover, is the placenta so inert with respect to this maternal force that it is not affected by it, as would be the case if the arteries were continued from the uterus into the veins of the placenta?

(5) Méry,[11] also states, in further support of the theory of reciprocal circulation, that if the respiration and vital force of the mother were not necessary for the fetal circulation, the fetus would be able to live as long in the uterus of the mother after her death as it is able to live after normal birth without any nourishment.

But all this is too vague and uncertain to be accepted as a fact, and before having to listen to this kind of reasoning, it is first necessary to inquire (1) whether any air passes from the mother to the fetus, (2) whether noxious particles return from the fetus to the mother, (3) what changes the fluids of the fetus undergo in the placenta and finally (4) what is the function of the placenta. All these things ought to be considered before we trouble ourselves about what is implied by such a dictum as Méry's or what can be said on each side of the question.

We are in fact not sure how long the infant survives after the death of the mother. According to Harvey [12] a fetus continued to live in the uterus some hours after the death of the mother and was then born alive. He says that a certain woman in his neighborhood was left dead in a locked room in the evening and on the following morning an infant was found between her thighs which he believes had made its way into the world by its own efforts,[13] and he adds that often in other women fetuses have survived that were removed from the uterus some hours after the death of the mothers.

(6) Finally it is said that quicksilver, tallow, and wax will pass from the arteries of the uterus to the veins of the placenta. If this were true and confirmed by experience it would be the strongest argument of all for a conjunction of the vessels. I shall, however, demonstrate, I hope easily, that this statement is false and contrary to all experience. Many writers say that they have seen this experiment done in various animals; but as I have shown before, only Noortwyk has done this in man. Drake, Vieussens and a few others say that they have filled the placentas of cows, dogs, and other animals with injected fluid, but they all seem to be mistaken about this, for the same experiment has afterward been done most carefully in the same animals and not a single drop was seen to pass into the vessels of the placenta from the uterus. Whoever reads Vieussens' book and notes how inconsistent it is and what an unusual, absurd, and completely unnecessary method of injecting quicksilver he reports he used, would certainly suspect that the man had never made an experiment,[14] for [after all] he clearly denies the anastomosis of the uterine vessels with those of the placenta, and thus nothing can be learned from the experiment which he did on the subject. This is all the more true because our own Monro Senior [15] did the same experiment twice with a better and more trustworthy

method, and found that although the vessels of the uterus and
its horns were filled with quicksilver, yet when they were opened
and the placenta, which is ring-shaped in those animals, was
separated (this is easily done) none of the injected material appeared in its vessels or those of the fetus.   Drake [16] mentions an
experiment done by Cowper, who says that the umbilical vessels
of a calf were filled from the uterine arteries of the mother through
the cotyledons; but Drake seems to be incorrect on this point, for
although Cowper himself speaks of certain preparations of these
organs he does not once mention an experiment of that kind.   In
the experiment which Monro [17] took the precaution to do much
more accurately on a cow, infusing fluids from the uterine arteries
toward the umbilical veins [18] and vice versa, he never saw the
slightest trace of fluid pass from one to the other.

Many others have tried the same experiment on the same animal, but no one ever used the same procedure as Drake says
Cowper did.

Slade says that he injected a dark liquid from the uterine arteries
through the cotyledons into the placenta, and in his own words
" the dark fluid passed into the substance of the placenta."   In
my opinion the fluid merely flowed over the uneven villous surface.

Monro [19] says that he looked for such an anastomosis completely in vain in cows injected with fluids prepared in various
ways, and that he could never be certain whether an anastomosis
of this kind exists at all in cows.

Heister narrates also that Cowper forced quicksilver into the
veins of the uterus through the umbilical arteries, but on consulting Cowper's own book we do not find that he had done or
seen this himself.   These are his words, " It appears that a kind
of inosculation may be made when quicksilver is injected "; and
in another place he says, " The two kinds of blood vessels seem
to communicate and mutually inosculate with each other," and
adds, " but he thinks that the whole thing seems to be too subtle
to permit summing up the experiments at the present time."   If
he had actually done experiments he would certainly have affirmed
with his usual vigor that he had infused quicksilver and seen it
pass to the uterus.   Finally Drake, who was aided by Cowper

himself in writing his book, would have mentioned the experiment if it had ever been done.

Noortwyk alone affirms that he had seen such continuous vessels and had filled the human uterus and placenta. Nothing indeed could support or advance this doctrine like an experiment of that kind done and confidently reported by such a fair-minded man. Anyone who heard him, however, would agree that our own Monro was correct and that Noortwyk deserved criticism; for Noortwyk [20] fell into an error from the beginning which deceived him through the whole experiment, and indeed he admits that when he separated the ovum from the uterus, the uterus and placenta adhered to each other so tightly that they could be separated only with the greatest difficulty.

On the contrary Monro never observed the uterus and the placenta adhering to each other so closely except perhaps in his first cases which he did not dissect accurately, and when mindful of his earlier error he dissected and examined four additional cases more accurately he always separated one from the other with no trouble. It thus appears that Noortwyk did not separate the uterus from the chorion but that he tore a part of the uterus, to which the ovum adhered, violently from the other part. This was the cause of a phenomenon which seemed to him new and remarkable, for he says that he did not see the openings on the whole lining of the uterus such as Albinus had demonstrated. It seems to me that Noortwyk had torn away these openings with the part of the uterus that he had separated from the rest. Monro found that in all four uteri dissected by him the chorion was always smooth, firm and tense and contained distinct vessels. If, therefore, this one error of Noortwyk in dissecting is conceded, we see the cause of all his new and unusual phenomena. All his other arguments collapse and if I am not mistaken we have a strong case for believing that the placenta is not joined to the uterus and that their respective vessels are not continuous.

But some one perhaps asks how Noortwyk can affirm that he had seen injected fluid appearing brilliantly red on the reverse side of the placenta. The answer is easy if we reflect that as everyone knows the placenta consists of a number of lobes between which a membranous thickening of the chorion is inserted in the same way as the pia mater is inserted into the sulci of the brain, and the soft substance of the uterus inserts itself into the sulci between these lobes. Granted that the uterus is everywhere filled with the injected fluid, what is there to prevent the latter from brilliantly shining through the reverse side where there is nothing over it except the transparent chorion and amnion? If, moreover, the terminal twigs of the placental veins receive the injected fluid, why, I ask, is that fluid not conveyed through the umbilical vessels to the fetus? Noortwyk never saw this implication himself. To banish even the shadow of doubt Monro undertook an experiment on this point.[21] Tying one iliac artery, he injected a very thin fluid through the other toward the uterus, with such force as to threaten rupture of the vessels. When he dissected the parts very carefully he could not find any trace of the fluid in the umbilical or fetal vessels.

Noortwyk, going still farther, says that even if the fluid does not penetrate from the uterus to the placenta " there may be, notwithstanding, a communication of the vessels."

Ruysch, although he could fill by injection through the spermatic vessels an unlimited number of arterioles coursing through the interstices of the seminal tubules and their lateral twigs which communicate with the seminal tubules, could not, however, force the material into the tubules themselves, although according to De Graaf, the arterioles are ten times smaller than the seminal vessels.

Noortwyk, however, can affirm nothing here nor add any confirmation of his doctrine. He merely objects to Monro's experiment on the ground that the vessels might communicate with each other without passage of the injected fluid. In all disputations, however, we should not ask for what might be, but for what is the case. Noortwyk was seeking an analogy in vain from De Graaf and Ruysch. De Graaf was totally wrong in his explanation of the seminal tubules, and it may be that the spermatic arteries first divide into much smaller branches than those which Ruysch filled with injected fluid, before they enter the seminal tubes. All that follows from this is that Ruysch was unable to force injected fluid into the smallest spermatic arterioles.

If the terminations of the spermatic arteries were as large as were the ends of the vessels seen in the lining of the uterus prepared by Noortwyk and if the beginnings of the seminal tubes were as large as the vessels of the uterus were according to him, I would not doubt that the fluid injected by Ruysch would penetrate into the seminal tubes, epididymis, the vasa deferentia, and other structures, just as Noortwyk would certainly have filled the umbilical vein and many other vessels with his injected fluid if that fluid had entered vessels as large as he thought them.

Having refuted, as it seems to me, all the arguments used to support the hypothesis that the arteries of the uterus are continuous with the veins of the placenta, I wish next to adduce a few on the other side, some of them drawn from the contentions of our adversaries themselves.

1. I think that there cannot be an anastomosis of vessels so unequal in size, for when the placenta is separated from the uterus we see vessels in its lining which can receive a goose quill, but no similar vessels are seen on the surface of the placenta. If the placental vessels were as large as those of the uterus how does it happen that they suddenly become so small that the very thin fluid which courses through the uterine vessels comes to a standstill and does not enter even a finger's breadth into them? Consider that the ends of the uterine vessels are a quarter of an inch in diameter and those of the placenta one-twelfth of an inch— in fact the difference between them is even greater—by what mathematical rule, I ask can the tube A, 1/4 inch in diameter, be continuous with tube B?

A ————————   ══════════ B

Who will say how this can be done?

2. If the vessels are continuous it is inevitable that they would all be ruptured and torn whenever the placenta is separated from the uterus, and many serious wounds would occur. In abortions or after birth at term, suppurations and purulent discharges would always appear. Yet we never see pus in abortions nor in the lochia after birth at term unless there are manifest signs of ulcera-

tion in the uterus or the vagina. If moreover the vessels were torn, more force would be required to separate the placenta than we observe in every day experience.

3. If there were an anastomosis of this kind the blood would flow from the cut end of the umbilical cord as long as the placenta remained attached to the uterus. On the contrary, as already stated, we never observe the loss of more blood than is contained in the cord.

4. If it is postulated that a reciprocal circulation is necessary and that the fetus is not able to generate red blood, how then do the fetuses of swine and of other animals in which the placenta is not connected to the uterus throughout pregnancy, receive nourishment and acquire red blood? Yet these fetuses are obviously nourished without any reciprocal circulation of blood. What stands in the way of believing that the human fetus is nourished in exactly the same way? Indeed, we observe red blood in the human fetus even before the placenta adheres to the uterus.

5. Those who argue in favor of the anastomosis thereby totally deny that the placenta has a function, for if the blood flows only through vessels it cannot be distributed through the substance of the placenta and thus be made suitable for nourishing the fetus. I have always thought, and not without reason, that the function of the placenta is to prepare the blood for the nourishment of the fetus.

6. Finally, the strongest and most important dictum is that a very thin liquid injected through the uterine arteries cannot be forced into the veins of the placenta. This has been the case whenever the experiment has been tried by the leading anatomists of this century, including in this city the two celebrated Monros, father and son, and in London Hunter and Mackenzie, the latter of whom has long taught the obstetrical art and the former anatomy with great distinction.

Mackenzie [22] dissected thirteen pregnant women injected with fluid. When he dissected one of these who was pregnant with twins, the very skilled anatomist John Hunter was also present. Although they worked with the greatest care and effort these observers could not see any of the injected material in the veins of the placenta or the fetal vessels. In two pregnant women fluid was injected through the umbilical vessels but not a single drop entered the uterine vessels.

After so many experiments conducted by such men as these in which the passage of injected fluid from the vessels of the uterus was never demonstrated, who, I ask, would think of adopting the contrary opinion? Or who will not judge with Monro that Noortwyk was wrong about this matter, however learned and fair-minded he is in general? No one but he asserts that he has seen such a passage of fluid, and with this error cleared up he would not again I think have reasserted that view.

I hope that I have finally shown beyond doubt that the uterine and placental vessels are not continuous with one another.

I shall now aim to explain how nutriment is transmitted to the fetus through the umbilical vessels. To my questioners I answer briefly, by absorption. They receive the nutrient fluid just as the roots of trees receive it from the ground through which they spread, or just as the lacteal vessels absorb the nutritive part of the food as it is carried through the intestine to be excreted. I assert, therefore, that the uterus adheres to the placenta by reason of the insertion of the soft substance of the uterus between the lobes of the placenta, and that elongated uterine vessels are everywhere in contact with the placental membrane. Since the uterine arteries which are in contact with the placental membrane surround the lobes of the placenta, in all likelihood the vessels which enter the placental lobes function as absorbents and receive that part of the blood which is suitable for nourishing the fetus.

There are a few who think that the uterine artery penetrates into the membrane which as I have said covers the surface of the placenta, and that the blood courses through it and is absorbed there. Their authority would have weighed heavily with me if they had published this conjecture and if it had seemed quite certain to them. I do not, however, find this conjecture sufficiently probable to accept it, for if the uterine vessels penetrated into the membrane after the separation of the placenta they would either be torn, leaving the placental surface rough and more or less ragged, or the vessels would be pulled out unevenly as if from so many foramina, some longer, some shorter according to the length of their course in the placenta. Such foramina should be easily visible. Neither one nor the other of these conditions occurs, and it is certain that no cavities of this sort filled with coagulated blood exist anywhere on the surface of the placenta.

If canals or portions of vessels remain in the substance of the placenta, as supposed by all who think that the membrane is perforated by the uterine vessels, is it not extremely remarkable that in so many cadavers, if the umbilical vessels are immersed in water and air is blown through them, it does not pass, nor can turpentine nor any other thin injected fluid be forced on through them, but on the contrary is exuded through the smallest tips of the placental vessels, not entering any such large vessels? Yet all these things [i. e., the escape of fluid injected via the maternal vessels (Translator)], are seen on the [inner] surface of the uterus although its great contractile force would be expected to compress the vessels and to annul these phenomena altogether, whereas no such power of compression and contraction exists in the placenta. Finally why are placental veins associated with the membrane (as proved when they are injected with turpentine) if the uterine arteries enter the substance of the placenta? And if indeed the arteries do cross, what can be said about their course?

Are any of the red particles absorbed? I am not as sure about this as of the absorption of fluid, but I think that red blood is not absorbed; first, because the vessels seem too small to be able to absorb it; second, because when the placenta of a cow is separated from the cotyledons, in which the vessels are much larger, nothing appears but a white fluid; third, because we do not see this kind of absorption anywhere in the rest of the body; and finally because it is not necessary, since we believe the fetus to be endowed with the power of making red blood. To what extent the placenta also assists in the work of making red blood, and functions like the lungs, or has other uses is quite another and irrelevant matter.

I think that the lymph is also absorbed by the placental vessels and taken into the placenta where it is mixed with the fluids that pass between the fetus and placenta, just as in adults the chyle is mixed with the blood circulating in the left subclavian vein. Whether that part of the blood which is unsuited for nourishing the fetus and is harmful is carried back to the mother through the arteries of the placenta cannot be stated at present. It seems, however, very likely to me, because it is analogous to the natural functions in other parts of the animal economy.

I would have added to what I have said about the union of the placenta with the uterus a few remarks about abortions, lochial discharges, and other diseases with which women are troubled during pregnancy and after birth, and would have drawn practical applications, had not the narrow limits of my discourse and lack of time prevented, forcing me to postpone those topics to another time.

And now as I come to the end of this slight essay I give thanks from the bottom of my heart to the very learned professors of this most flourishing institution for their great generosity and benevolence to me, and since they never failed in diligence or doctrine or skill in teaching as long as I studied with them, I promise as far as I am able the greatest diligence and labor in the healing art, that I may not be unworthy of them nor do harm to the sick. Finis.

REFERENCES

(Shippen's references, followed by translator's amplification in parentheses.)

1. *Ed. Med. Ess. vol. ii* (Alexander Monro Senior, in Medical Essays and Observations, Revised and Published by a Society in Edinburgh, 6 v., 1733-44, and subsequent editions).
2. *Prim. Lin. 8c9* (Albrecht von Haller, Primae lineae physiologicae, Göttingen, 1751 and subsequent editions).
3. *Comp. Anat., p. 136* (Laurenz Heister, Compendium anatomicum, 1719 and subsequent editions in Latin and English).
4. *Adv. an. 4.476* (Johannes Baptista Morgagni, Adversaria anatomica omnia, 1719 and subsequent editions).
5. *Harv. Exercit. 56* (William Harvey, Exercitationes de Generatione Animalium, London, 1651 and subsequent editions in Latin and English).
6. *In praelect.* (William Hunter, in his oral lectures).
7. *In praelect.* (Alexander Monro Junior, in his oral lectures).
8. *Hist. Uteri grav.* (Willem Noortwyk, Uteri humani gravidi anatome et historia, Leyden, 1743).

9. *Mem. Acad. Sci. 1708* (Jean Méry, in Mémoires Acad. roy. d. Sciences, Paris).
10. *Mem. Acad. Sci. 1708* (Pierre-Simon Rouhault, ibid).
11. *Mem. Acad. Sci. 1708* (Méry, see ref. 9).
12. *Exerci. de Partu* (William Harvey, De partu, published with his Exercitationes de generatione animalium; see ref. 5).
13. *Ex de uter. et memb.* (William Harvey, De membranis ac humoribus uteri, published with his Exercitationes de Generation Animalium; see ref. 5).
14. *De Struct. uteri, etc. 51-56* (Raymond Vieussens, Dissertatio anatomica de structura et usu uteri et placentae muliebris. Published as supplement to Philip Verheyen, Supplementum Anatomicum, sine Anatomiae corporis humani liber secundus, Cologne, 1712).
15. *Ed. Med. Ess. vol. ii.* (Monro Senior; see ref. 1).
16. *Phil. Trans. No. 281* (James Drake in Philosophical Transactions of the Royal Society of London, 1702, pp. 1217-1240, Discourse concerning some influences of respiration on the motion of the heart, hitherto unobserved).
17. *Med. Ess. vol ii* (Monro Senior; see ref. 1).
18. *Idem.*
19. *Ed. Med. Ess. vol. ii* (Monro Senior; see ref. 1).
20. *Hist. gravid. ut.* (Noortwyk. see ref. 8).
21. *Med. Ess. vol ii* (Monro Senior; see ref. 1).
22. *In praelect* (Colin Mackenzie, in his oral lectures).

Appendix II

A

From *The American Museum*, Philadelphia, 1790, vol. 8.

*The following short address, shewing the advantages of con-
ferring the degree of doctor of medicine in the first instance,
and pointing out a proper plan of a medical education, was
delivered at a commencement lately held in the college of
Philadelphia; by William Shippen, jun. M. D. professor of
anatomy and surgery in the university of Pennsylvania and
college of Philadelphia; fellow of the royal college of physicians at Edinburgh, censor of the college of physicians, at
Philadelphia, and member of the American philosophical
society.*

UPON a subject of so general importance to the community,
as the medical education of its youth, no apology can be
wanting, for a public address—nor should the smallest change in
the forms already established, take place without a public appeal.
All ages have agreed as to the danger of innovations: and the
sanction derived from precedents, has generally been proportioned
to their antiquity: but in this case, as in all other rules, there must
be exceptions; and it need not be remarked, that the wisest systems
have grown to perfection by degrees, and that without the aid of
innovations, no system almost would have deserved the epithet
of wise.

Since our last commencement in this place, a change in the form
of conferring degrees, has been adopted by the learned and benevo-
lent fathers of this seminary, which I propose to explain and
justify.

Until now, the highest medical honours have never been conferred upon students in the first instance. Whatever might have
been their genius—whatever their industry—and however qualified by these, and the knowledge which had been the consequence

147

of them, for the attainment of every reward in our power to give, they were obliged to stop at a bachelor's degree, being all the honour we could bestow, and to practise three years, with reputation, in that subordinate capacity, before they could be raised to a higher one.

Experience is the mother of truth; and by experience we learn wisdom. It is thus that we have discovered, that the mode hitherto practised, has been objectionable; and we have endeavoured to amend it. 1st. It has been generally observed, that those gentlemen who have received bachelor's degrees (particularly those who have settled in the country) have been careless at the end of the three years practice, as to their advancement in the college; for in that time they have either established a reputation, that satisfies them, or have been convinced, that another degree would add but little to it, among a people who have had an experimental knowledge of their abilities; and thus have neglected those advantages and those honours, which it would have been their right to demand, and our pride to bestow. In the second place; such gentlemen, as have been ambitious of obtaining a doctor's degree, have been obliged, at great expense and greater inconvenience, to repair to foreign universities, where doctor's degrees are given to any who are thought properly qualified to receive them. Add to this, the country has been liable to deception; for they do not enquire what degree a student has received; he is ever a doctor with them; and that he has taken a degree has been always sufficient to convince them that he is worthy of their confidence.

It may also be worthy of observation, that a young student is never so well qualified to pass the necessary examinations for a doctor's degree, as just after he has been industriously employed in the medical schools; nor is it easy or convenient to spare so much time from his practice, as may be necessary to comply with the rules of the college. As the degree of knowledge necessary to entitle a person to a doctor's degree is greater than that which is expected from a bachelor, so the mode of trial and examination is different; in order to obtain a bachelor's degree, it was only necessary to have a competent knowledge of the Latin language and natural philosophy—to live three years with a physician—to have attended one course of lectures upon anatomy and surgery, chymistry, materia medica, and the theory and practice of physic. He was then admitted to a private examination before the faculty and trustees: if approved, he was called to a public one, which was nothing more than an abridgment of the former. Whereas to be honoured with a doctor's degree, all these requisites are insisted upon, and in addition to them, they must attend a course of lectures on botany, and remain two years in the medical school before they be admitted to examination and trials, very different from the former. For first, they are to be severely examined, and strictly scrutinized, in private by the faculty, on philosophy, and all the branches of medicine—then a case is given to them, of a disease, of which they are to point out the cause, symptoms, the indications and method of cure: next a question is propounded, either anatomical, surgical, chymical, or physiological, which they are to answer and explain in writing. If these be approved of, they are admitted to a public examination, upon all the different branches of medicine: and to conclude the whole, it is required of them, to write a dissertation on some medical subject, and defend the doctrine and principles it contains, against any of the faculty, in the language in which it is written.

Thus a sort of medical ordeal is established, from which it is difficult to escape without being qualified to receive the honours which they solicit—and thus we shall save those young gentlemen, who wish the highest degrees, the trouble and expense of going abroad, while we gratify their patriotism by giving them equal advantages at home.

I should be unjust both to the university and the college, as well as to those gentlemen, who have formerly graduated in both, if in shewing the advantage of conferring doctor's degrees in the way now proposed, I did not acknowledge, that great attention had been paid to the students, and that they had come forward duly qualified to receive their degrees under the former establishment. Indeed it must have been remarked, that in pointing out the differences between the two, I enumerated the requisites, which have been always necessary to the attainment of a bachelor's degree, and that in doing so, I shewed the care and attention which must have been paid: and I would beg leave further to remark, that the principal advantage we propose to ourselves, is the facilitating the access and smoothing the way to doctor's degrees in this country: for many purposes and in many cases a bachelor's degree may be desirable; and the former mode was fully competent to the acquiring that degree: but it was to be wished, that those gentlemen, who had time, industry, and abilities to entitle them to doctor's degrees, and who were ambitious of obtaining them, might easily be gratified; and this alteration we hope will have effected it.

These young gentlemen, whom we present this day to the public as worthy of their confidence, and with whom we think the health of their fellow citizens may safely be entrusted, have in a short time qualified themselves for the high honour they are now to receive, by a close application to study, and by unwearied diligence, which, although they can surmount almost all difficulties, would not have been sufficient, if, instead of mispending two or three years, as the young gentlemen from the country generally do, in reading books upon subjects which they can have no proper ideas of, without demonstrations and experiments, they had not begun and prosecuted their studies in the following regular and proper mode. After having acquired such a knowledge of the Latin language as enabled them to read any medical author, and attended to such branches of the mathematics and natural philosophy, as are connected with, and necessary to the study of medicine, they began their medical enquiries with reading the book of nature, and by attending a course of anatomical lectures, by which they became acquainted with the structure, situation, and use of the several parts of the human body, whose diseases they wish to prevent and cure. Any medical or surgical knowledge, not built on this basis, will be false and insecure; and I would earnestly advise, that no book on the theory and practice of medicine, be ever put into the hands of a medical student, till he be well acquainted with anatomy.

In the next place, they learned pharmacy, chymistry, and physiology, by attending the lectures of the careful and ingenious Wistar.

They acquired a knowledge of the materia medica from the lectures of the sagacious and learned Kuhn,* and the accurate and sensible Griffitts—and were taught botany by the ingenious Barton —and having thus laid the best foundation, they finished the superstructure by a close attention to the prælections on the theory and practice of physic delivered by the able and experienced Rush.†

I should now proceed, gentlemen, to enjoin the necessity of future attention to your business, in order to become, indeed, blessings to your country; to remind you, that although you have, by a close application to your elementary studies, qualified yourselves for the highest honours, that the profession you have chosen, affords, and passed with reputation and success, the examination which leads to them, a great deal remains to be done, and that it depends on your exertions in future, to entitle you to that glorious appellation of relievers of the distresses of mankind—The elegant Tully says—

" Homines nulla re propius ad divos accedunt quam salutem hominibus dando ": But that I leave with the greatest confidence to our learned provost, who will point out to you the course of your duty with much more ability, than I can pretend to. Attend to his precepts, and take with you my best wishes for your happiness and success.

---

* Dr. Kuhn is now professor of the theory and practice of physic in the university of Pennsylvania.

† Those young gentlemen, whose circumstances will not permit their living in Philadelphia during the whole course of their studies, should make a point of spending one season there, and attending one course of lectures upon anatomy, and one on the materia medica, previously to their apprenticeship in the country; and this may be done at the small expense of 20 guineas, boarding &c. included.

B

EXAMINATION OF MEDICAL CANDIDATES

The Pennsylvania plan for examination of medical candidates was closely modeled upon the scheme in operation at the Medical School of the University of Edinburgh in the eighteenth century. What this procedure was like has been accurately described by Samuel Bard in his letter of May 15, 1765 to his father Dr. John Bard of New York. William Shippen's experience, four years earlier, of which we have no extant account, would have differed only in detail. Bard's letter [1] follows:

The day before yesterday I received my degree with all the form and ceremony usual upon such occasions. The two Monros with Dr. Cullen were in all my private examinations. My good friend, Dr. Hope, publicly impugned my thesis; and to all of them I consider myself much indebted for their behaviour upon this occasion in which although they kept up the strictness of professors they never lost sight of the politeness of gentlemen. My examinations were as follows: on the first day I had not the most distant hint what was to be the subject of my trial. I went in, I confess, trembling, and Dr. Cullen began my examination by asking me some general definitions, as *quid est medicina?*, and so on; he then went on to the structure of the stomach and alimentary canal, thence made a digression to their diseases, with their diagnosis and method of cure. Then young Dr. Monro followed upon similar topics. This ended my first examination which lasted near an hour. My next consisted in writing commentaries upon two aphorisms of Hippocrates, and defending them against old Dr. Monro and Dr. Cullen which took up an hour also. My last private one was writing commentaries upon two cases in practice, much in the same manner as those I sent which I defended against young Dr. Monro and Dr. Cullen. This examination took an hour and a half; and lastly I was called upon publicly in the hall, to defend my thesis. During all these trials, my exercises were not only written in Latin but I was obliged to defend them in the same language; not even in the first, where I was ignorant of my subject, being allowed to speak a word of English.

[1] MacVickar, 69.

INDEX

Names of authors and authorities appear in italics, with page number of first reference to each work cited.

153

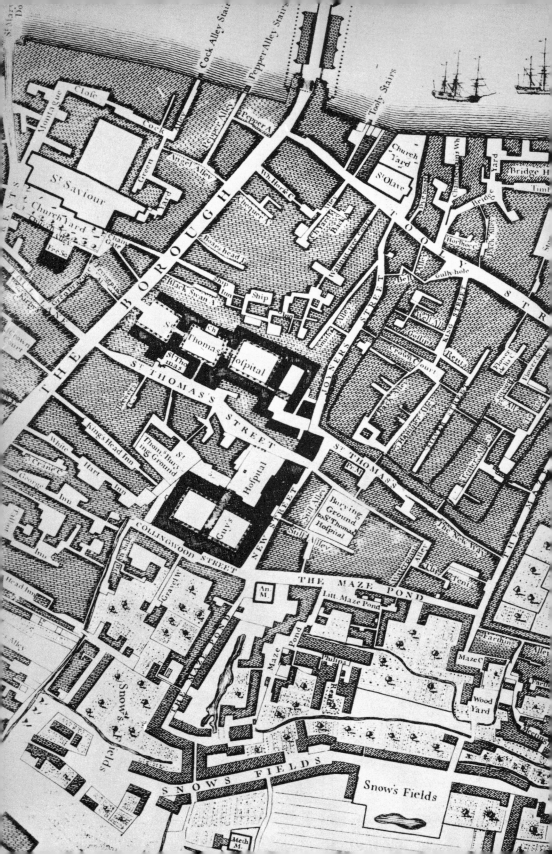